FIELD GUIDE TO THE

CRADLE *of* HUMANKIND

STERKFONTEIN, SWARTKRANS, KROMDRAAI
& ENVIRONS WORLD HERITAGE SITE

BRETT HILTON-BARBER PROF. LEE R. BERGER

foreword by THABO MBEKI

DEDICATION

TO JAMES AND IMOGEN,
MEGAN AND MATTHEW

PUBLISHED BY STRUIK NATURE
(AN IMPRINT OF RANDOM HOUSE STRUIK (PTY) LTD)
REG. NO. 1966/003153/07
CORNELIS STRUIK HOUSE, 80 MCKENZIE STREET, CAPE TOWN 8001
PO BOX 1144, CAPE TOWN, 8000 SOUTH AFRICA

VISIT US AT **WWW.RANDOMSTRUIK.CO.ZA**
LOG ON TO OUR PHOTOGRAHIC WEBSITE
WWW.IMAGESOFAFRICA.CO.ZA
FOR AN AFRICAN EXPERIENCE

FIRST PUBLISHED 2002
SECOND REVISED EDITION 2004
5 7 9 10 8 6 4

PUBLISHING MANAGER: PIPPA PARKER
MANAGING EDITOR: HELEN DE VILLIERS
EDITOR: PIERA ABBOT
DESIGNER: JANICE EVANS
ILLUSTRATIONS P. 87, 89, 92, 94, 96 & 139–99:
WALTER VOIGHT © CRADLE OF HUMANKIND FIELD GUIDE TRUST (CHT)
ADDITIONAL ILLUSTRATIONS AND MAPS: DAVID DU PLESSIS

REPRODUCTION BY HIRT & CARTER CAPE (PTY) LTD
PRINTED AND BOUND BY CRAFT PRINT INTERNATIONAL LTD

ISBN 978 1 77007 065 3

PICTURE CREDITS & COPYRIGHT ©

GALLO PICTURES (G); MUSEUM AFRICA (MA); THE SOUTH AFRICAN LIBRARY (SAL); STATE ARCHIVES (SA); NATIONAL AERONAUTICS AND SPACE ADMINISTRATION (NASA); GAUTENG GOVERNMENT (GG); STRUIK IMAGE LIBRARY (SIL); PETER M. FAUGUST, DEPARTMENT OF ANATOMICAL SCIENCES, WITS MEDICAL SCHOOL (PF); NATIONAL GEOGRAPHIC (NG); TREVOR SAMPSON/BUSINESS DAY (TS/BD); IAN JOHNSON (IJ); TOM HUFFMAN (TH); NIC BEUKES (NB); UWE REIMOLD (UR); PAULINE ROWLES (PR); RICHARD DU TOIT (RDT); ROCK ART RESEARCH INSTITUTE, WITS UNIVERSITY (RARI); CRADLE OF HUMANKIND FIELD GUIDE TRUST (CHT)

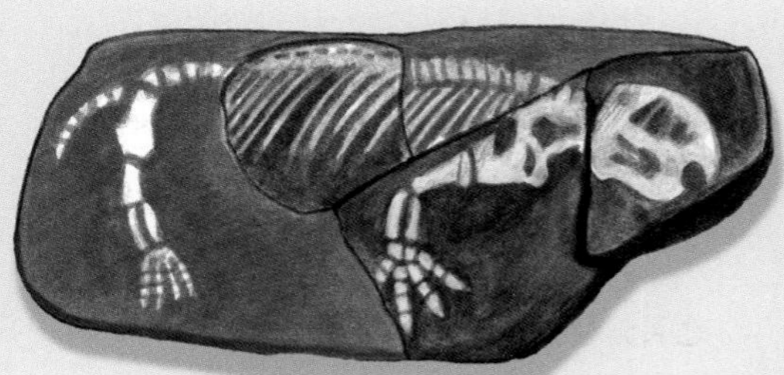

ABBREVIATIONS USED IN THE BOOK

COH CRADLE OF HUMANKIND
BCE BEFORE COMMON ERA
MYA MILLION YEARS AGO

CONTENTS

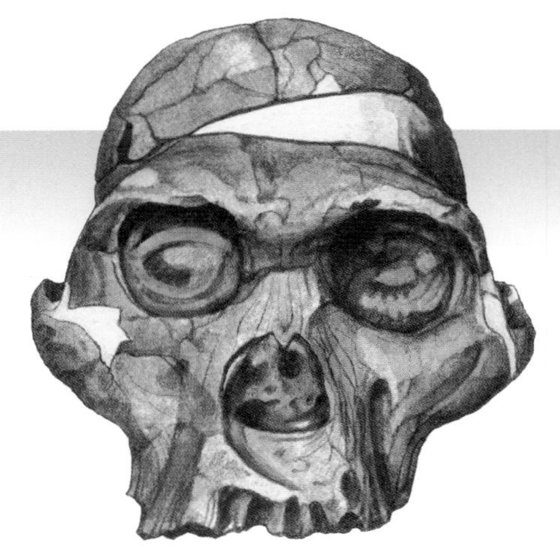

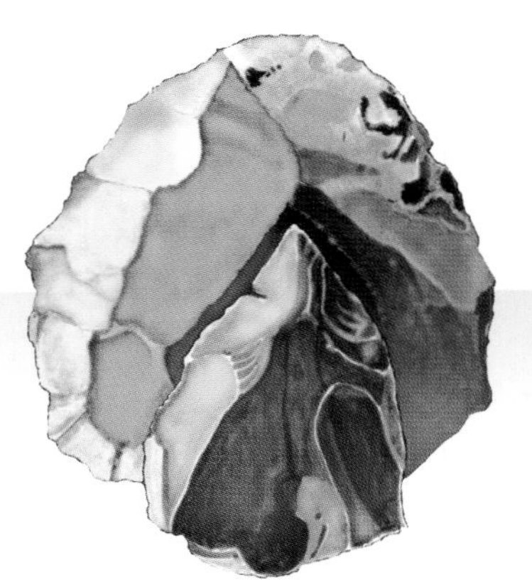

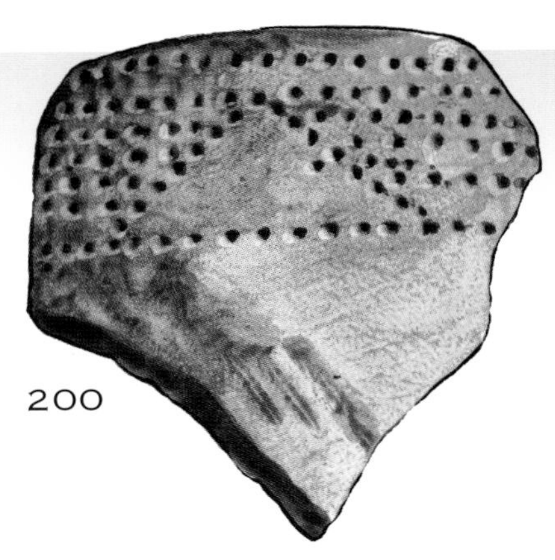

FOREWORD BY THABO MBEKI

In the introduction to his book, *The Origin of Species*, published in 1859, Charles Darwin cautioned his peers not to be surprised about some of the missing links in the relentless pursuit of information on the exact nature of the origin of species, including the human species. He wrote:

> *No one ought to feel surprise at much remaining as yet unexplained in regard to the origin of species and varieties, if he makes due allowance for our profound ignorance in regard to the mutual relations of all the beings which live around us. Who can explain why one species ranges widely and is very numerous, and why another allied species has a narrow range and is rare? . . . Although much remains obscure, and will long remain obscure, I can entertain no doubt, after the most deliberate study and dispassionate judgement of which I am capable, that . . . species are not immutable; but that those belonging to what are called 'same genera' are lineal descendants of some other and generally extinct species, in the same manner as the acknowledged varieties of any one species are the descendants of that species. Furthermore, I am convinced that Natural Selection has been the main but not exclusive means of modification.*

Since Darwin made these observations 143 years ago, many questions have been answered. Exhaustive and meticulous research by dedicated teams of archaeologists, palaeontologists and other scientists has unveiled many mysteries about the geological formations and evolution of our Earth and the origin of living organisms, including the beginnings and development of human beings.

These painstakingly thorough investigations form part of humanity's quest to understand itself. This process can be likened to an odyssey that has taken scientists to the far reaches of our planet, where they have dug deep into the bowels of the Earth in order to uncover the truth.

In addition to rigorous physical journeys, these scientists have also undergone a concomitant intellectual journey through a labyrinth of different beliefs, some asserting the interposition of an omnipotent, miracle-making deity, others postulating models of the causes and effects of matter.

South Africa has made an important contribution to this odyssey since 1858 – a year before Darwin published *The Origin of Species* – when Thomas Holden Bowker collected stone artefacts among sand dunes near the Great Fish River in the Eastern Cape, some of which were donated to the Royal Artillery Museum at Woolwich, London, and were returned almost 100 years later.

Important work by John Goodwin, Peter van Riet Lowe, Raymond Dart, Robert Broom, Phillip Tobias, Alun Hughes, Ron Clarke, Bob Brain, Lee Berger, Francis Thackeray, André Keyser, Kevin Kuykendall and many other eminent scientists has ensured that South Africa has contributed immensely to humanity's search for knowledge.

This book, *The Field Guide to the Cradle of Humankind*, by Brett Hilton-Barber and Lee Berger, is itself an important contribution to the understanding of human evolution and emphasizes the centrality of South Africa and other countries on the African continent in unravelling the important subject of our origin. Through this book and others by scientists here and abroad, we are able to proclaim that humanity emerged in the highlands and savannas of the vast African continent. As a result of rigorous investigations by numerous scientists, we now know that:

- Africa is the oldest and most enduring of all the continents;
- the earliest living organism discovered thus far, 3,6 billion years old, comes from Barberton in Mpumalanga, South Africa;
- the earliest dinosaur egg was found in South Africa;
- the Karoo in South Africa has an unparalleled sequence of fossil deposits;
- South Africa and other African countries have yielded fossils that prove humans originated in Africa, and that it was here that they first walked on two feet and developed the ability to adapt continuously to changing environs;
- it was on the African continent that our early human ancestors developed larger brains relative to other primates;
- modern technology originated in East Africa, where the first stone tools were manufactured and used;
- our early human ancestors first controlled and made fire in South Africa.

These evolutions and innovations by humanity, much of which are evident from the various fossil sites in the Cradle of Humankind, have enabled humanity to colonize the entire world, and develop a variety of great civilizations at different points in our history.

Despite these crucial contributions to humanity, Africa today is poor and underdeveloped, the result of a brutal slave trade and subsequent colonial and neo-colonial plunder.

After many years of struggle to liberate Africa from colonialism and apartheid, the entire continent is now on the threshold of a great renaissance. We seek to ensure that Africans live and enjoy better and prosperous lives, regain their dignity and self-respect and occupy pride of place as equals among the people of the world, no longer subservient to any of their fellow human beings.

Accordingly, as Africans, we must overcome the debilitating effects of an unjust past that sought to inculcate the notion that black people are by nature inferior. In the past, Africans have been made to hate themselves, lose faith in themselves, and encouraged to leave their destiny in the hands of others. This book should help Africans to realize that, having given birth to humanity, we must reverse the many years of dehumanization that have characterized our recent past.

This book can therefore be viewed both as celebrating successes in the study of humanity's ancestry and as a medium for instilling confidence in Africans to ensure that, for Africa, the next century will be one of rapid change, development and prosperity.

As Africans, we have agreed on a plan, the New Partnership for Africa's Development (Nepad), to ensure that the vision of a developed and prosperous Africa becomes a reality.

One of the strengths of this book is that it is accessible to the majority of our people, with many photographs, illustrations, explanations and easy-to-read text. This underlines the importance of ensuring that all our people, especially children and the youth, have access to this information and understand the true meaning and value of its message.

It is hoped that our investment in the development and improvement of the Cradle of Humankind World Heritage Site will give the people of the world an opportunity to better understand their own origin, evolution and development into sophisticated modern human beings.

This is one of the ways in which we as South Africans can contribute to a world free of racism, of hatred, conflicts and wars, a world based on mutual respect, dignity and human solidarity.

This book will make an important contribution to the success of this historic project.

Thabo Mbeki.

THABO MBEKI
State President SOUTH AFRICA 2002

FOREWORD BY MARK READ

Lying about 40 kilometres from the centre of Africa's economic powerhouse is a stretch of highveld grassland and mixed woodland that has caught the imagination of the world. This seemingly unremarkable area has been awarded the highest conservation status of World Heritage Site by UNESCO, and as such will forever be designated as belonging to *all* the people of our planet. The *Sterkfontein and Environs World Heritage Site* is an area of about 48 000 hectares in extent. It is not blessed with large rivers, vast monuments or mountain ranges. Luckily, it is still in an almost pristine state, yet to the uninformed it can be an entirely forgettable area through which small streams run between shrubby banks. Plant diversity is high and so too are the number of bird species, particularly in summer. But the reason for the site's special status lies not in its external beauty, but rather beneath the ground – in the dolomites.

The Sterkfontein site overlies a vast mass of ancient limestone that formed when the Earth was half as old as it is today. At the surface of the dolomites, caves emerged, and associated with these caves are some of the world's richest fossil deposits. Bones of ancient animals attest to a time when the Earth was fundamentally different. These fossil riches also contain the gems for which all palaeontologists search – the rarest of the rare – the bones of our earliest ancestors. In all likelihood no objects in the world have stimulated as much scientific argument and resultant discourses as the fossilized remains of Africa's early hominids. South African fossils have contributed hugely to the vast scientific database that has accumulated. But until now very little information has been available to the general public. This book seeks to fill that void.

The revised edition of the *Field Guide to the Cradle of Humankind* is a remarkably concise and informative book that seeks to inform readers about the unique biological and geological wealth of the area. It is an ambitious guide because it aims to educate the interested layman about perhaps the most fractured and fractious science of all – the story of our own lineage and pedigree. Palaeoanthropology (the study of ancient mankind) is a fluid science because so few fossils have been found and each new find often brings with it a new theory as our family tree grows bushier and bushier. Indeed the world's richest site for ancient hominids is Sterkfontein, which, through the work of our eminent scientists, has contributed vastly to contemporary theories about our own evolution. The fact that they still remain theories renders this book all the more fascinating. It is also this book's biggest weakness, as theories can change and are obviously totally subjective. It is therefore inevitable that often valid criticisms are aimed at an attempt such as this to explain our origins to the layperson. New editions will differ fundamentally from earlier ones as the authors respond to emerging information and new discoveries.

This new edition seeks not only to respond to the market need for such a book, but also to address the criticisms levelled at the first edition. It incorporates new information and contemporary hypotheses on hominid evolution. While not seeking to please everyone, the book has evolved into a concise and accurate publication, which will guide thousands of visitors through one of the most fascinating corners of our beautiful country.

MARK READ
PAST (Palaeo-Anthropology Scientific Trust) – *Vice Chairman*

A view of the Motsetse site. (IJ)

PREFACE

Standard Bank is committed to the future of Africa. The continent is a potential economic giant that needs to be kindled and nurtured. We support President Thabo Mbeki's view that we all need to make this a century of growth, development and success for Africa. We are a South African and African bank, and we will grow and prosper far more easily if our continent is successful. Doing what we can to help Africa realise its potential is therefore central both to our approach to business and to our interactions with our staff and the wider community.

Recent discoveries by leading South African researchers on the origins of humankind have again put this part of the continent under the global spotlight and sparked fascinating scientific debates. They have provided an opportunity for South Africa to further enhance its standing in the international community. We are all indebted to the dedicated researchers who have built up a remarkable record of discoveries through their patient and persistent efforts over many decades to unlock the secrets of early humankind.

The ancient heritage of the origins of man is precious to all of humanity. Testimony to this is the value placed on Sterkfontein and environs by the United Nations when it declared the Cradle of Humankind a World Heritage Site. From a local perspective, we should not disregard current and potential associated benefits such as tourism and a heightened awareness of the need to care for the environment.

Our bank is pleased to include research into the origins of humankind as one of the cultural heritage projects that we support. Standard Bank has been a pioneer as corporate supporter of the study of human evolution and the preservation of heritage in southern Africa. We are the major sponsor of the Palaeo-Anthropology Scientific Trust (PAST), to which we have pledged millions of rands for the ongoing study of human origins and evolution in Africa. Our association with PAST resulted in the bank donating 100 hectares of its cultural heritage farm, Mogale's Gate, to the Gauteng provincial government, custodian of the Cradle of Humankind World Heritage Site. The land is to be used for the establishment of a world-class interpretation centre, the first port of call for visitors to the Cradle of Humankind. This is one of our many contributions to Africa's renewal, and we will continue to work closely with those who contribute their skills and energies to the continent's development and growth.

As the oldest bank in South Africa, our fortunes are bound up with those of our country and our continent. It is crucial for our success that Africa should succeed. We certainly intend to do what we can to contribute to the renaissance of Africa in the 21st century.

South Africans have a rich cultural heritage to acknowledge, celebrate and share with the international community. This book by Brett Hilton-Barber and Lee Berger is one significant medium of communicating the real Africa to the rest of the world. So, page through. Take a historic journey, venture into Africa's re-awakening spirit and celebrate with us a remarkable story of determination and success.

DEREK COOPER
Chairman, Standard Bank

ACKNOWLEDGEMENTS

The authors would like to thank Standard Bank and the Gauteng Department of Agriculture, Conservation, Environment and Land Affairs (DACEL) for their sponsorship and support of this field guide. The sponsors see this book as the first of many such publications and want to encourage and support further initiatives such as this.

The views and opinions expressed in the book are not necessarily those of DACEL or Standard Bank. The authors are ultimately responsible for the layout and content of the book, and although DACEL and Standard Bank have had the opportunity to comment on the manuscript prior to it going to press, any errors or omissions are the responsibility of the authors.

The authors are indebted to professors Paul Dirks and Bruce Rubidge, doctors Judy Maguire and Darryl de Ruiter – all of Wits University – as well as Nico Grobler from the Gauteng Directorate of Nature Conservation for general advice on content. Grateful thanks are extended to Simon Hall, Christine Read and Christa Clusters for helping improve on the first edition. From an illustration perspective, our thanks go to Walter Voigt and John Gurche, and to Ian Johnson for his photography. Others who assisted in the project are Susan Joubert, Libby Young and Mark Read.

This book would not have been possible without the support of the following: President Thabo Mbeki and the South African Government, Tourism and Environment Minister Mohammed Valli Moosa, the premiers and provincial governments of Gauteng and the North West Province, the Gauteng Department of Agriculture, Conservation, Environment and Land Affairs – specifically its MEC Mary Metcalfe, Director General Trish Hanekom as well as Joanne Yawitch, Frank Ledimo, Steve Baylis, Craig Whittington Jones and Sue Taylor. Sincere thanks go to the Cradle of Humankind Unit within DACEL, headed by Michael Worsnip who is assisted by Melinda Swift and Tshimangadzo Nemaheni. Acknowledgement is due to Terry Timson, Richard Steyn and Khanyi Mlambo who have been part of the Standard Bank team; the South African Heritage Resource Agency; the trustees of the Palaeo-Anthropology Scientific Trust and its many donors; the National Geographic Society; the landowners in the Cradle of Humankind and the communities that live within it; the University of the Witwatersrand; the Northern Flagship Institution; the University of Pretoria; the University of Arkansas; the University of Zurich; Duke University; the staff and students of the Palaeoanthropology Unit for Research and Exploration (PURE); the field staff of the Sterkfontein Research Unit; the excavators and field technicians at all sites for their efforts and making the discoveries happen. Thank you too to the Struik team of Pippa Parker, Piera Abbott, Janice Evans, David du Plessis, Colette Stott and Helen de Villiers.

Lee Berger would like to acknowledge his wife Jackie and his children, Megan and Matthew, for all their love and support. Brett Hilton-Barber would like to thank Josie for her support and patience in allowing this work to be completed in between the rigours of raising a new family. Others who have assisted in ways they may not know are the Hilton-Barber family of Tana, Dave, Steven, Monica and Bridget, Martin Miller, Mary Ann Cullinan, Pauli and Murray Grindrod, Paul Jenkins and Michelle Magwood, Mike Kirkinis, Revil and Tamar Mason, and the Hole in the Head Gang.

JULY 2002

INTRODUCTION

The 47 000 hectare Cradle of Humankind is a unique location blessed with a greater wealth of the prehistory of humankind than almost any other place on Earth. Officially called the Sterkfontein, Swartkrans, Kromdraai and Environs World Heritage Site, the Cradle contains more than 12 major fossil sites and dozens of minor ones that present us with an intriguing mixture of mystery and revelation about much of our ancient past.

Sterkfontein Valley. (IJ)

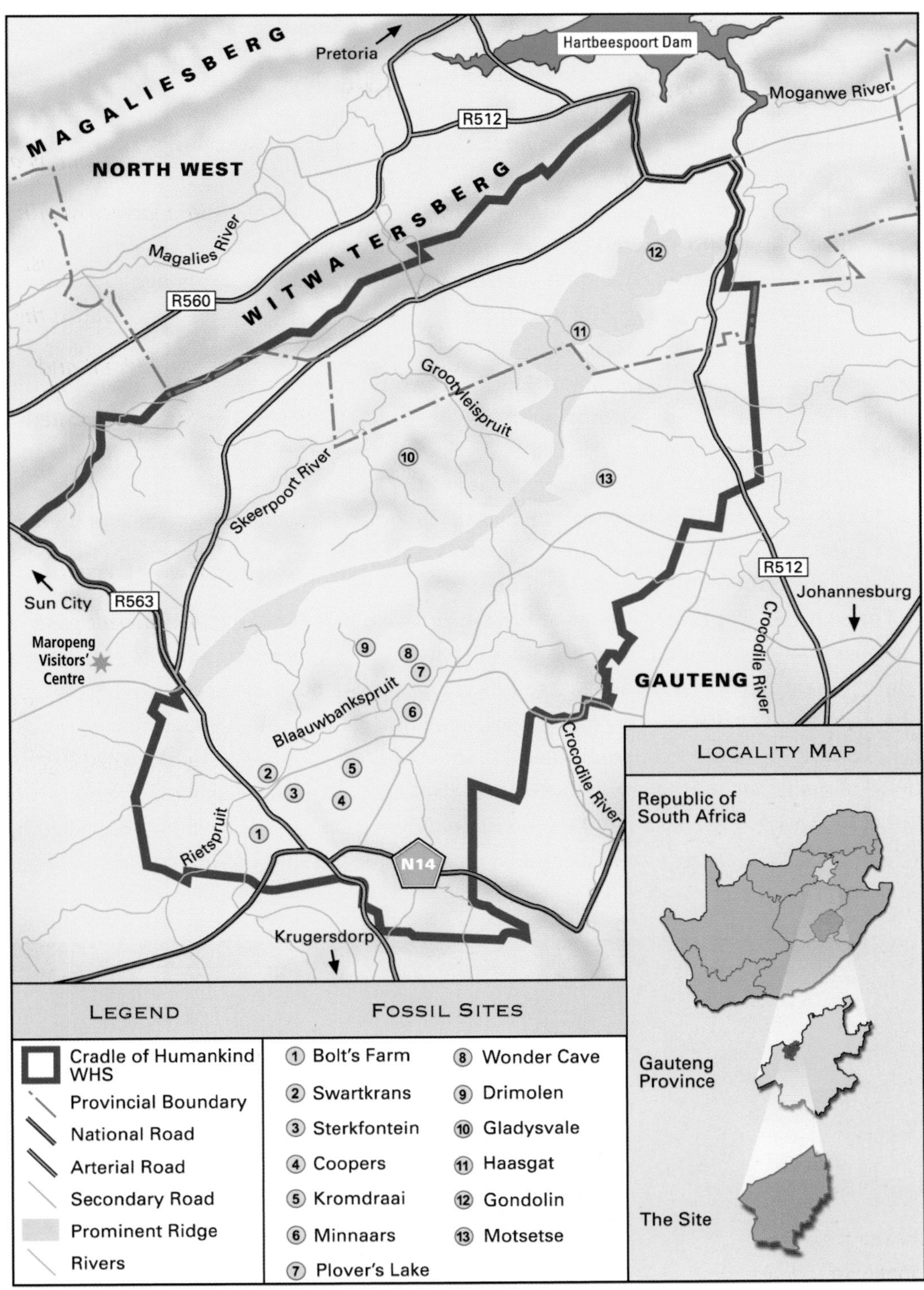
MAGALIESBERG
Pretoria
Hartbeespoort Dam
Moganwe River
R512
NORTH WEST
WITWATERSBERG
Magalies River
R560
Grootvleispruit
Skeerpoort River
R512
Johannesburg
Sun City
R563
Maropeng Visitors' Centre
GAUTENG
Crocodile River
Blaauwbankspruit
Rietspruit
N14
Krugersdorp
LOCALITY MAP
Republic of South Africa
Gauteng Province
The Site
LEGEND
Cradle of Humankind WHS
Provincial Boundary
National Road
Arterial Road
Secondary Road
Prominent Ridge
Rivers
FOSSIL SITES
1 Bolt's Farm
2 Swartkrans
3 Sterkfontein
4 Coopers
5 Kromdraai
6 Minnaars
7 Plover's Lake
8 Wonder Cave
9 Drimolen
10 Gladysvale
11 Haasgat
12 Gondolin
13 Motsetse

The Cradle of Humankind lies in the Witwatersrand Basin on the edge of the divide between the highveld grasslands and the more vegetated bushveld in the South African province of Gauteng. It is a summer rainfall area where the higher lying reaches are rolling grassland while the well-watered valleys have thick riverine bush thinning into mixed woodlands on the slopes.

Beneath the 2,6-billion-year-old dolomitic hills found in the Cradle of Humankind lies a series of extensive underground caverns. These geological time capsules have preserved the fossil remnants of tens of thousands of extinct animals, as well as the bones and cultural remains of our own ancestors, the hominins.

Included in the Cradle of Humankind is the world-famous Sterkfontein Cave, which has become synonymous with the South African search for human origins. It is located in the dolomitic bedrock underlying the region. This bedrock was once an ancient sea bed and the valley contains some of the world's oldest undistorted rocks, dating back to between 2,6 and 2,8 billion years. That is just over half the age of the Earth itself!

The dolomites are the sedimentary remains of an ocean floor that hosted some of the earliest forms of life on Earth – prehistoric blue-green algae. These can still be seen in the rocks today in the form of fossilized stromatolites.

Through the ages the area now designated the Cradle of Humankind has undergone a number of changes. Giant inland seas have come and gone, meteorites have struck near it and dinosaurs have roamed across its surface. The climate has varied considerably, but for the past 3 million years or so, during what scientists call the Plio-Pleistocene (the period when much of human evolution occurred), there has been less variation. During the early stage of the Plio-Pleistocene the Cradle of Humankind enjoyed a subtropical environment. It became much drier as a result of global cooling, yet it has always been conducive to hominin occupation because of the availability of water and shelter, and the varied animal and plant life.

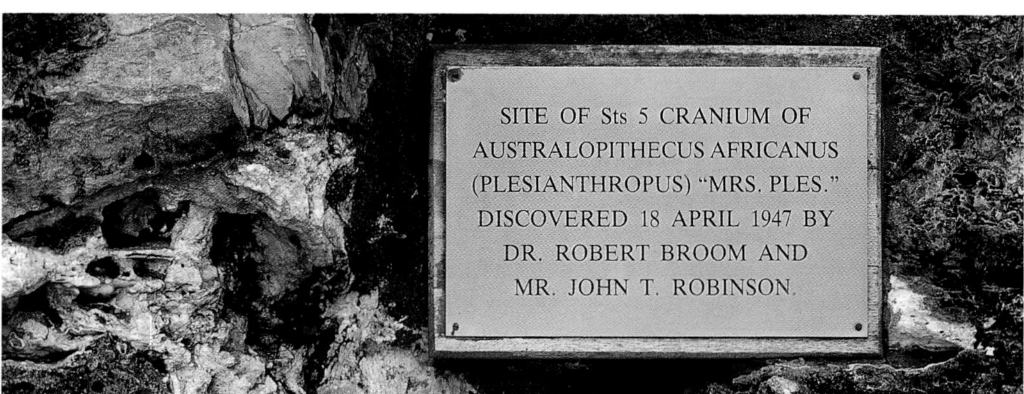

HOMININ VERSUS HOMINID

Humans and their ancestors have generally been referred to as hominids in the literature of the recent past. Of late, however, a new, scientifically more appropriate term has come into play, namely 'hominin', which will be used in this book.

Linnaeus, the father of classification.

In 1758 botanist Carolus Linnaeus (or Carl von Linné) developed a binomial classification system that uniquely identified different animals and plants. This system is still used today, albeit in a modified form. Animals are classified, in descending order, into the following taxa: kingdom, phylum, class, order, family, genus, species.

In the Linnaean system of classification, organisms with similar morphological characteristics were grouped together. Thus, humans are classified firstly within the kingdom Animalia (as opposed to Plantae); then in the phylum Chordata because we have a hollowed dorsal notochord (the primitive precursor of the backbone); as part of the Mammalia class because we have hair and suckle our young; as Primates because we share with apes, monkeys and lemurs certain morphological characters; and as Hominidae because of certain characteristics that differentiate us from the apes, for example bipedalism (the ability to walk on two legs). Our generic classification, *Homo*, designates us as human and our species name, *sapiens*, means, rightly or wrongly, 'wise'.

The Linnaean classification system also makes provision for superfamilies, which are a subdivision of a suborder, and subfamilies, which are a subdivision of a family. The superfamily Hominoidea (hominoids) includes all the living apes. This is the starting point of the present debate on classification.

The traditional view has been to recognize three families of hominoid: the Hylobatidae, the Hominidae and the Pongidae. The Hylobatidae include the so-called lesser apes of Asia, the gibbons and the siamangs. The Hominidae include living humans and closely related fossil apes, such as the australopithecines, that possess certain characteristics, for example bipedalism, reduced canine size and increased cranial capacity. The Pongidae include the remaining African apes and the orang-utan, whose 'apeness' is recognized in the fact that it is a large-bodied, tail-less, quadrupedal, arboreal primate.

THE MOLECULAR CLOCK

The study of genetics has introduced a new factor into the study of human ancestry. Scientists have been able to isolate certain nucleotides and amino acids within the DNA chain and have measured their rate of mutation. Based on the assumption that this mutation takes place at a consistent rate, they have been able to map out the timelines in the diversification of those species sharing a common genetic framework. Chimpanzees and humans, for instance, share over 97 per cent of their genetic make-up. By plotting the rate of mutation of genes in apes and humans, scientists have attempted to work out when the two species diverged from a common ancestor. Although the study of genetics is a young science and is open to interpretation, it appears to confirm what palaeontologists are discovering in the field – that the lineages of apes and humans diverged at some time between 5 and 7 million years ago. Research has also shown that Africans have a greater genetic diversity than any other ethnic grouping, which implies that they are the world's oldest peoples – there has been more time for genetic mutation to occur. This is strong evidence that all modern humans descended from a single population that lived in Africa between 100 000 and 200 000 years ago.

Recent genetic research suggests that humans are much more closely related to two other members of the family Pongidae, the common chimpanzee and the bonobo, than either of these species are to the gorilla. We share almost 98 per cent of our genes with chimps, which indicates that humans share a recent common ape ancestor with the chimpanzees. Divergence times between the two groups based on a molecular clock suggest that the chimpanzee/human split occurred between 5 and 7 million years ago, which is much closer to the present time than the chimpanzee/gorilla split.

The African apes are more closely related to one another than any of them are to the orang-utan. In turn, humans, chimps, gorillas and orang-utans are more closely related to one another than they are to the gibbons and siamangs. In recognition of these genetic relationships, some scientists argue that we must overhaul the present morphologically based classification system and replace it with one that is more representative of our true evolutionary relationships as evinced by our genes.

This is where the term 'hominin' comes into use. Under this proposed classification model, Hominoidea would be a primate superfamily, as has always been the case. Orang-utans, gorillas, chimps and humans would fall under this hominoid umbrella in the family Hominidae. In recognition of their genetic divergence some 11 to 13 million years ago, the orang-utans would be placed in the subfamily Ponginae and the African apes, along with humans, would all be lumped together in the subfamily Homininae.

The bipedal apes, namely living humans and all their fossil ancestors, would fall into the tribe Hominini (thus hominin). All the fossil genera, such as *Australopithecus*, *Ardipithecus*, *Kenyanthropus* and most of the *Homo* species, would be grouped in this tribe. A few of the more extreme evolutionary biologists want to include humans and chimpanzees within the same genus, *Homo*, but most scientists agree that this is taking the line of reasoning too far.

As to the debate on whether to use the term 'hominin' or 'hominid', the growing pervasiveness of genetics in every aspect of our modern lives means that the term hominin will probably win out in the long run. It has many advantages in its precision and in its recognition of a biological reality that moves beyond physical morphology.

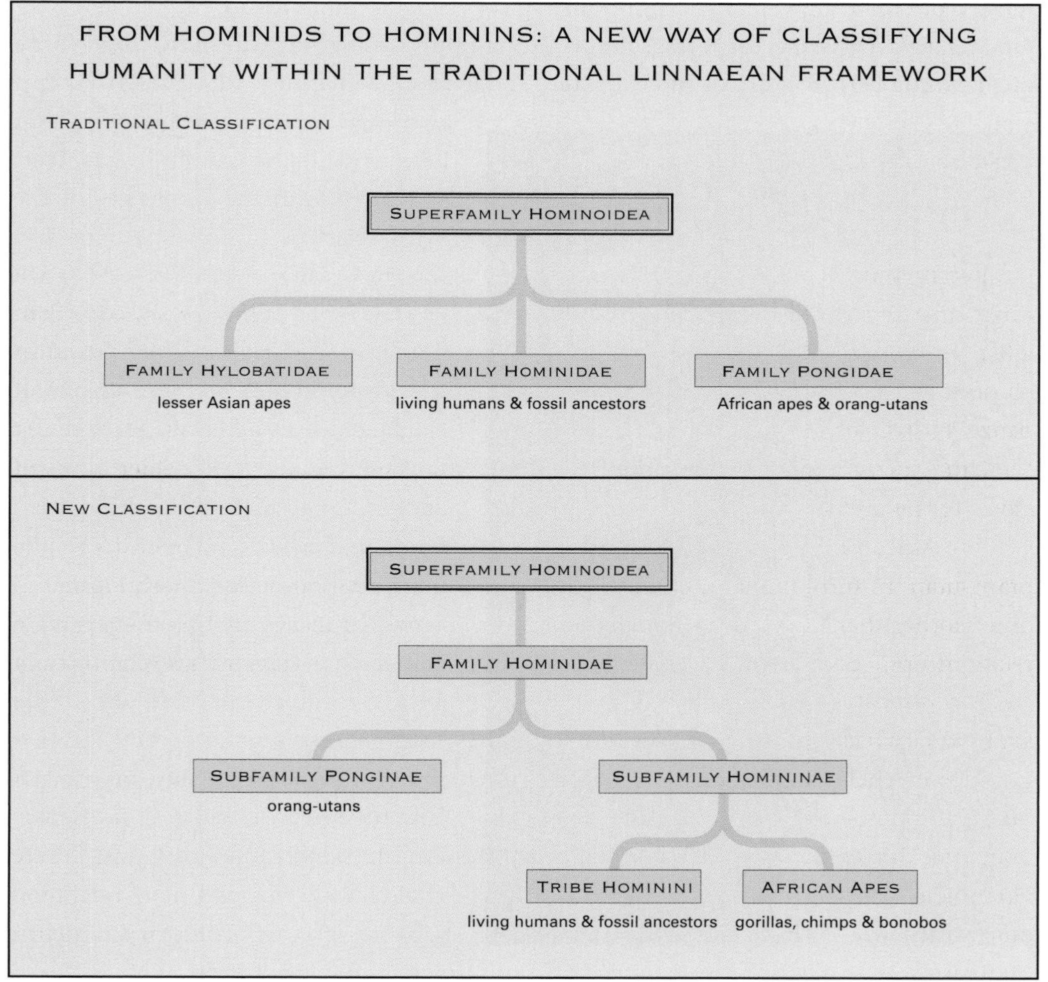

STERKFONTEIN – A KEY TO UNLOCKING THE MYSTERIES OF THE PAST

It is a commonly accepted scientific assumption that we are the latest product of an evolutionary chain that split from the ancestral apes somewhere around 5 to 7 million years ago. There is incontrovertible fossil evidence that this split occurred somewhere in Africa, which is often referred to as the Cradle of Humankind. At least 13 different hominin species that evolved since the split have been identified, and discoveries of their remains have been concentrated in two main areas – East Africa and South Africa.

While the finds in East Africa have been scattered through several countries, mainly Tanzania, Kenya and Ethiopia, the key to understanding human origins from a South African perspective is located mainly in the Sterkfontein area. This small piece of Earth has, remarkably, yielded over 35 per cent of the world's early hominin fossils.

Sterkfontein itself is the world's longest running archaeological excavation, having been dug continuously for the past three decades, and excavated intermittently during the three previous decades. Excavations have been undertaken mainly by scientists associated with the University of the Witwatersrand in Johannesburg and the Transvaal Museum in Pretoria.

Chimps share almost 98% of our genetic make-up. (G)

Five or possibly six different hominin species have been found at the various sites in the Cradle of Humankind. In addition, three major tool cultures and a wide range of plant and other animal fossils have been found that provide a framework for the interpretation of human evolution.

What makes the Cradle of Humankind such a tremendous repository of ancient fossil treasure? The answer is a complex one. One important factor is the geological personality, or coincidence, of the area, which is favourable for the preservation of fossils. These vital clues to our past have withstood millions of years of the vicissitudes of environmental change.

A CAVE IS FORMED

Generally, caves in the Cradle of Humankind have followed six stages of cave formation:

Stage 1: A cavern forms through the dissolution of dolomite in what is known as the phreatic zone, the zone beneath the water table. Its original shape is usually determined by faults or planes of weakness in the rock.

Stage 2: The water table drops, usually because of the natural erosion, or cutting, of a nearby valley and the cave becomes filled with air. Stalactites and stalagmites now begin to form in the cave as surface water continues to percolate through the dolomite.

Stage 3: Avens, or shafts, start forming and gradually begin to approach the surface.

Stage 4: Avens break through to the surface. A talus cone may begin to form beneath the opening, filled with dirt, organic debris and bones of animals derived from the surface. If this cone becomes calcified by lime-bearing water dripping from the ceiling it is cemented into what we term 'cave breccia'.

Stage 5: The cave is almost completely filled with cave breccia and the entrances begin to expand as a result of erosion.

Stage 6: During this final stage erosion or mining has de-roofed the cave entirely and the bone-bearing breccia is exposed.

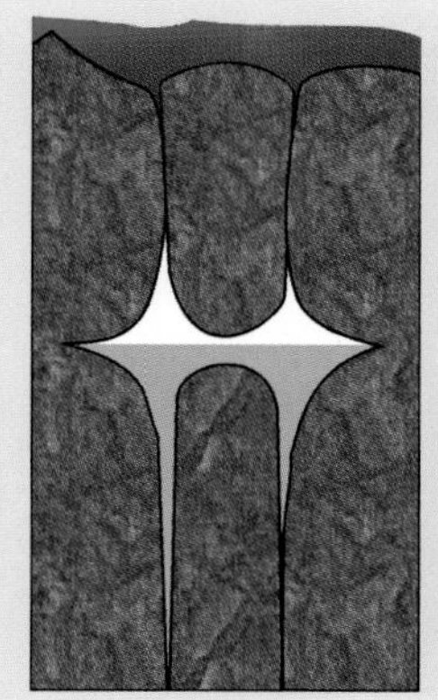

Stage 1

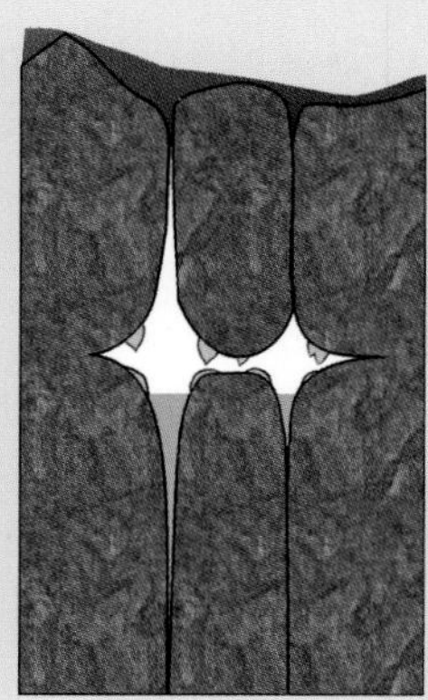

Stage 2

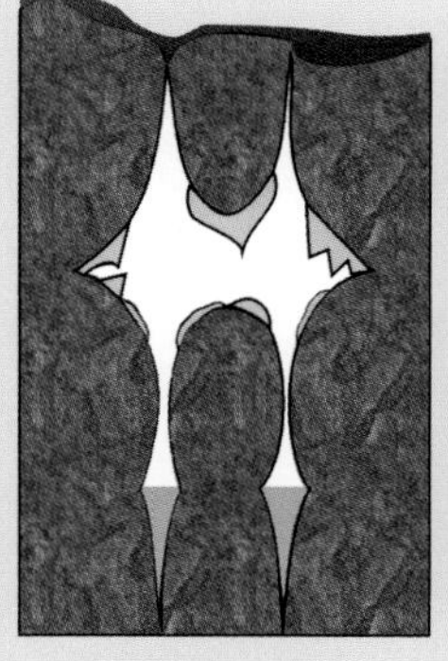

Stage 3

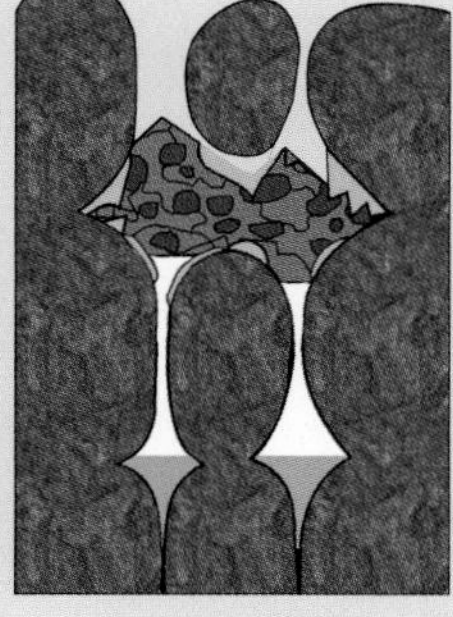

Stage 4

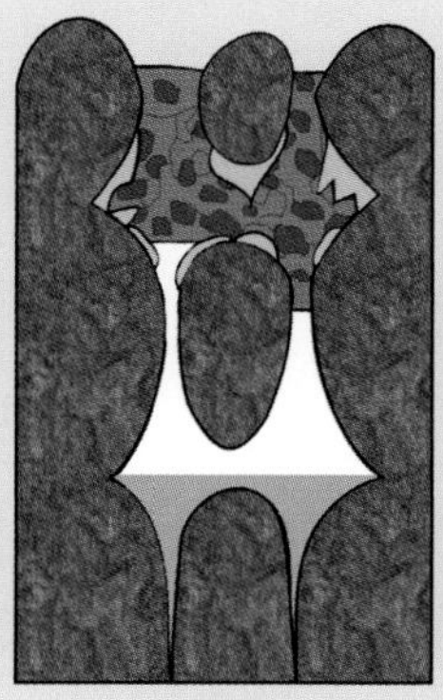

Stage 5

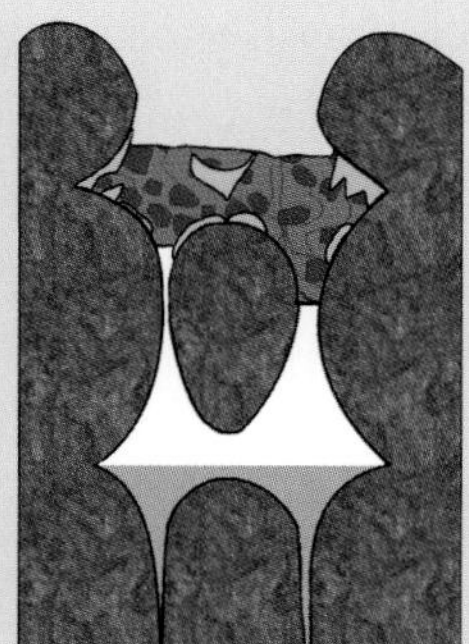

Stage 6

THE MAKING OF A FOSSIL

The word 'fossil' is derived from the Latin *fossilis*, 'something dug up'. Fossils are the preserved remains of, or image of the remains of, a once living organism such as an animal or a plant. Even the traces left by a once living organism, such as footprints or trackways, are considered fossils.

Typically, fossils are recorded in sedimentary rocks that have been laid down by the actions of water. Fossilization is the process whereby an organism is transformed into a fossil. It usually involves the impregnation of pores and holes in the remains of the organism with minerals in solution. Minerals like calcium carbonate and silica are some of the more common fossilization agents, preserving bone for millions of years.

In other situations, water seeping through rocks may dissolve away the remains of an organism, leaving a cast of the original form. This cast is itself a 'trace' fossil, but it may be filled by other minerals transported by groundwater to create a replica of the original. Hard tissues such as bone or shell have a greater chance of surviving the fossilization process than soft parts like muscle, fat and hair.

In the Cradle of Humankind, most fossils are preserved either as casts or as permeated and replaced bones, but almost every other type of fossilization has occurred here, including the preservation of trackways in wet mud on cave floors and the preservation of leaves in piles of mulch. The most common mineral found in the fossilization process of this area is calcium carbonate that has precipitated from the surrounding dolomitic bedrock.

No fixed time of burial is required for the remains of an organism to be declared a fossil, but there is general consensus that some level of mineral replacement needs to have taken place.

Precipitating limestone in Wonder Cave. (IJ)

Over time, dolomites erode and create pockets within themselves. Calcium carbonate, or limestone, the main component of the dolomitic bedrock, precipitates in these extensive pockets. When lime-rich solutions infiltrate the sand or bones on cave floors a form of concrete called breccia is formed. The breccia facilitates the long-term, stable and safe preservation of the remains of animals, and of ape-men.

While this has ensured that the quality of fossils from the Sterkfontein area is very good, the topsy-turvy stratigraphy of cave infills has made the actual dating of fossils a difficult and often controversial task.

The fossils themselves are extraordinary – not only the individual pieces, but the sheer volume of fossil fragments that has emerged from the various sites. More than 1 000 hominin fossil fragments, several hundred thousand animal fossils, 300 fragments of fossil wood and over 9 000 stone tools form a vast, multi-dimensional and continually expanding scientific jigsaw puzzle. These finds provide a compelling picture of the last 3,5 million years of South African prehistory.

Although several pieces of the puzzle are missing, and may never be found, there is growing evidence that modern humans may well have evolved in the southern part of Africa.

In brief, the puzzle that has been put together so far tells the following story: between 2 and 3 million years ago, a hominin with a blend of ape and human characteristics occupied the Gauteng highveld, seeking shelter in the riverine forests and foraging for food in the broken woodland. This ape-man, known by the scientific appellation of *Australopithecus africanus*, may well have been the ancestor of our own genus *Homo*. Standing approximately 1,3 metres tall, with a brain about the size of a grapefruit, *A. africanus* lived in small social groupings, eking out a living from a subtropical landscape dominated by predators such as the false sabre-tooth cat *Dinofelis*, and populated with other now extinct creatures like the hunting hyena, giant leaf-eating monkeys and small primitive baboons.

The consequences of far-reaching climatic change between 2 and 3 million years ago created evolutionary pressure on the ape-men living in the Cradle of Humankind.

Excavations at Sterkfontein bear witness to an intriguing phenomenon, the speciation window, that occurred between 2,5 and 2 million years ago when the morphology of one species began taking on the characteristics that would eventually lead to a separate species. Around this time, a certain population of *africanus* may have started to take on characteristics associated with the robust ape-man (a flatter-faced, larger-toothed australopithecine), while another population began to resemble the earliest members of our own genus, *Homo*. Just after this happened, *africanus* apparently disappeared from the fossil record. Intriguingly, however, the early *Homo* species and the robust ape-man appear to have co-existed for hundreds of thousands of years, each grappling with rudimentary tool technology and occupying different ecological niches.

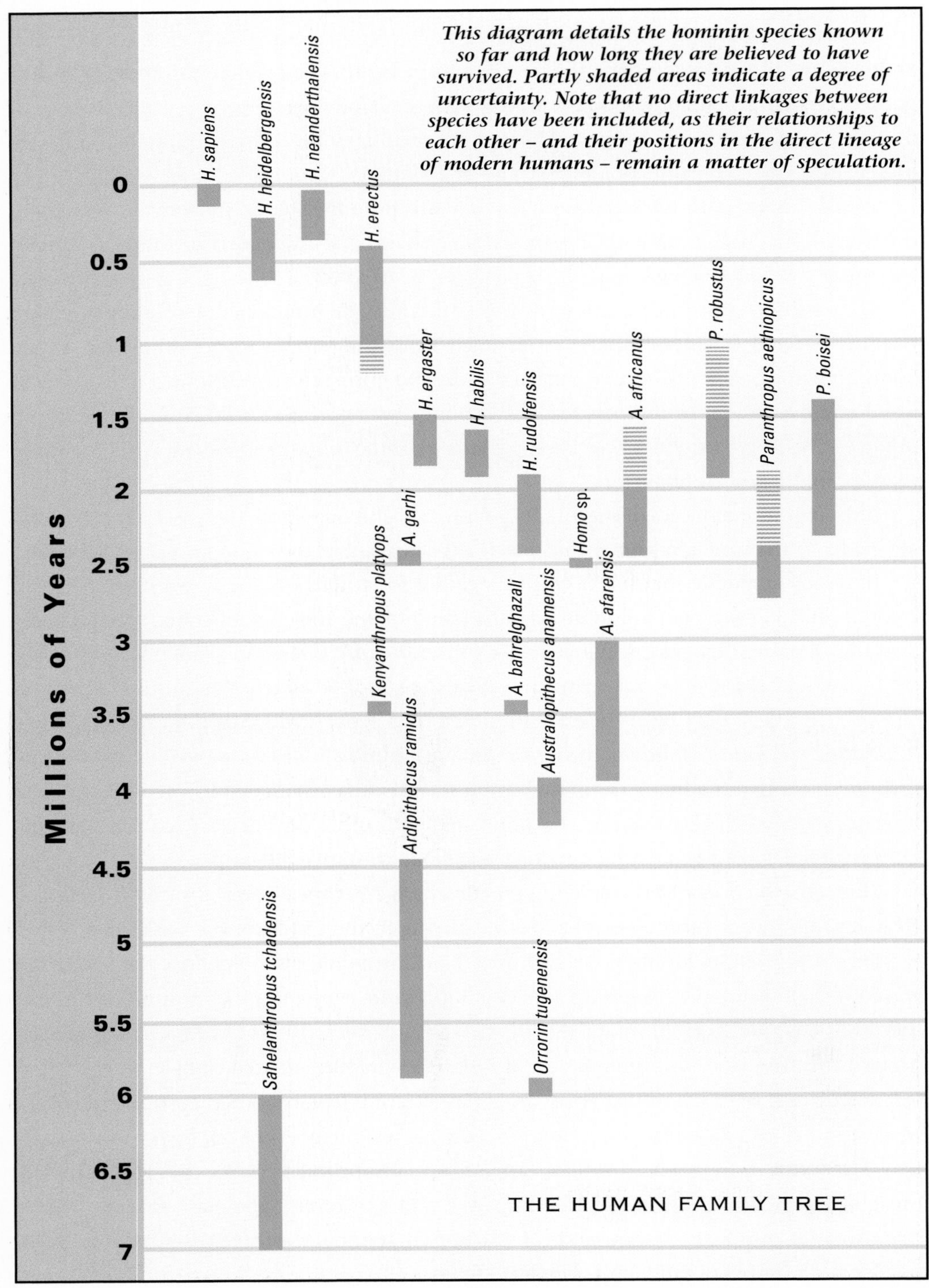
This diagram details the hominin species known so far and how long they are believed to have survived. Partly shaded areas indicate a degree of uncertainty. Note that no direct linkages between species have been included, as their relationships to each other – and their positions in the direct lineage of modern humans – remain a matter of speculation.
Millions of Years
0
0.5
1
1.5
2
2.5
3
3.5
4
4.5
5
5.5
6
6.5
7
H. sapiens
H. heidelbergensis
H. neanderthalensis
H. erectus
H. ergaster
H. habilis
H. rudolfensis
A. africanus
P. robustus
Paranthropus aethiopicus
P. boisei
A. garhi
Homo sp.
Kenyanthropus platyops
A. bahrelghazali
Australopithecus anamensis
A. afarensis
Ardipithecus ramidus
Sahelanthropus tchadensis
Orrorin tugenensis
THE HUMAN FAMILY TREE

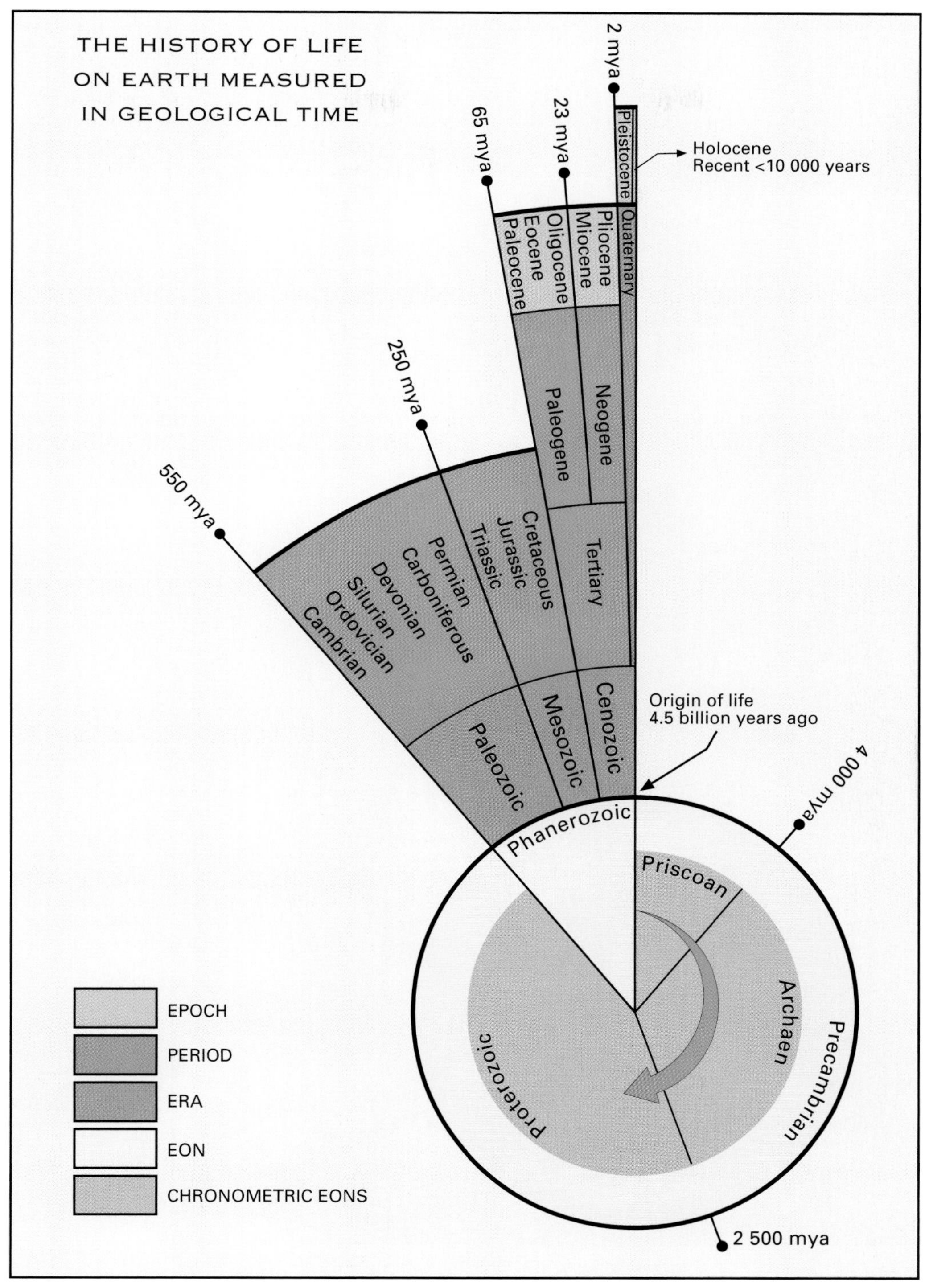
THE HISTORY OF LIFE ON EARTH MEASURED IN GEOLOGICAL TIME
2 mya
23 mya
65 mya
250 mya
550 mya
Pleistocene
Holocene
Recent <10 000 years
Quaternary
Pliocene
Miocene
Oligocene
Eocene
Paleocene
Neogene
Paleogene
Tertiary
Cretaceous
Jurassic
Triassic
Permian
Carboniferous
Devonian
Silurian
Ordovician
Cambrian
Cenozoic
Mesozoic
Paleozoic
Origin of life
4.5 billion years ago
4 000 mya
Phanerozoic
Priscoan
Archaen
Precambrian
Proterozoic
2 500 mya
EPOCH
PERIOD
ERA
EON
CHRONOMETRIC EONS

Artist's impression of an encounter between early* Homo *and the robust ape-men. (NG)

It appears that the robust ape-men could make use of bone tools – there is evidence that they used these at the sites of Swartkrans and Drimolen, while it appears that early *Homo* was responsible for the manufacture of stone tools, of which thousands have been found in the Cradle of Humankind, the earliest dating back to around 2 million years ago. But even these ideas may change in the light of new discoveries. There is emerging evidence from sites like Coopers, for instance, that many of the early stone tools may in fact have been made by the robust ape-men, and not by early *Homo* as had previously been thought.

The early *Homo* species, most commonly known as *Homo habilis*, were larger brained than both the robust and gracile australopithecines and were also more opportunistic – their varied diet meant that they developed superior hunting and scavenging skills, whereas *Australopithecus robustus*, which had a largely vegetarian palate, did not develop these skills. By 1,5 million years ago there was a noticeable change in stone tool technology that may indicate that *Homo erectus* was beginning to replace *habilis*.

At Swartkrans, a short distance from the Sterkfontein caves, there is even evidence that *Homo erectus* began to tame fire approximately 1–1,5 million years ago. It is not clear if this was captured fire or manufactured fire, but most scientists believe that this may be the first evidence of an ability to 'steal' fire from natural bush fires caused by lightning, and transport the flames into caves for warmth and protection.

Over time, *Homo* populations flexed their mental and social superiority, slowly coming to dominate the harsh and competitive environment of the African bushveld and eventually, around 1,5 million years ago, migrating northwards out of Africa and occupying habitable environments in Europe and Asia.

Around 1 million years ago, the robusts had followed the earlier ape-men into extinction, unable to survive in a world where the available niches were increasingly being filled by *Homo*. The story of *Homo*'s dominance and the inability of the robusts to evolve outside their specialist habitats can be found in the artefacts and bones of the Cradle of Humankind. In many ways, it is the story of our success as a species.

There is convincing evidence that the *Homo erectus* populations that remained in Africa evolved into an archaic form of *Homo sapiens* between 800 000 and 200 000 years ago. Although the fossil record is sparse in this regard, it would appear that archaic *H. sapiens* was the first species to transform communication into recognizable language and to take on the trappings of contemporary human behaviour. Remains of archaic *H. sapiens* are to be found in the Cradle of Humankind, although the best evidence comes from the western Cape coastline and the central Free State.

These pre-modern humans laid the foundation for the origin of our own species between 200 000 and 100 000 years ago. There is strong circumstantial evidence that this transition took place in southern Africa.

PART ONE

OF BLOOD *and* STONE

This guide is designed around the premise that people are mostly shaped by their environment. Our bodies and minds are not of recent origin. They are the direct consequence of millions of years of surviving in Africa and adapting to the dramatic changes this continent has seen in the course of the last 5 million years. Africa has shaped not only our physical bodies, but the societies within which we live. The way we interact today at a social and cultural level is in many ways the result of organizational skills developed by our hominin ancestors in Africa over millions of years.

It is important to remember when reading about the 'recent' history of the Cradle of Humankind that the area has been occupied by humans, or their ancestors, for the past 3 million years at least.

History is a particularly sensitive subject in South Africa, where racial, ethnic and cultural differences have been used as justification for social discrimination. Given South Africa's most recent history of institutionalized racism, the concept of ethnicity is a loaded one, and yet we have to recognize that it has been one of the key drivers in African social development.

This part of the guide reflects on the ethnic origins of the people who today live in the vicinity of the Cradle of Humankind and attempts to do so in an objective manner. It describes the recent historical forces that have played themselves out against this landscape, forces that in many ways have shaped South Africa in its entirety. It then dissects the extraordinary geological framework of the landscape to explain how the Cradle of Humankind can be read like a prehistory textbook. Finally, it chronicles the search for human origins at Sterkfontein and the surrounding sites, providing the reader with a context in which to understand the animal and hominin species that existed long ago in this very special part of the world.

CHAPTER
one

CROSSROADS IN TIME

Who were the original South Africans to occupy this part of the country? This question begs another one: exactly how far back do we want to look? Humans and their biological ancestors have lived on the subcontinent for the past 3,5 million years at least. For the past few thousand years the area has been a convergence point for different cultures, races and language groupings.

The San hunted in the wooded valleys of the Cradle of Humankind until they were displaced by the arrival of Bantu pastoralists from the north. Then the Iron Age ancestors of the present-day Sotho/Tswana built a dynasty that lasted nearly seven centuries before it was torn apart by the waves of tribal instability known as the Difaqane and the Mfeqane. The subsequent social vacuum was dominated by European settlers, whose political relationships were determined by a desire for sovereignty, the subjugation of indigenous tribes and exploitation of the world's richest gold fields.

FROM HUNTER-GATHERERS TO GOLD MINERS

The South African interior has always had its attractions. From the dawn of humanity the climate of the area has been generally temperate, allowing the australopithecines to flourish in the gallery forests and broken woodland. As our genus, *Homo*, emerged over millions of years, the well-watered river valleys and bushveld provided ample game and shelter against the elements. The hunter-gatherer lifestyle was refined in this region, which is evident in the artefacts that have survived in the numerous caves found in the dolomitic outcrops.

The pastoralists migrating southwards from Central Africa found the rolling grasslands good for their livestock, first sheep and then cattle. There was enough stone to build their villages and water to sustain growing communities. The first Iron Age miners found that there was an adequate supply of iron ore in the landscape and sufficient trees to burn in order to work the raw iron into weapons and tools.

THE ORIGIN OF RACE

Race is a very sensitive issue, more so in South Africa than almost anywhere else. However, human races are not as different as people may sometimes think. Any two humans – of any ethnic background – living anywhere in the world are genetically more similar than any other similar mammal species, for example two chimpanzees living in different troops in different regions in Africa.

(PR)

Scientists believe racial diversity is a relatively recent evolutionary phenomenon that arose in response to our ancestors occupying different climatic zones during the past 50 000 years.

Having originated in Africa, our earliest ancestors were almost certainly dark-skinned, their pigmentation protecting them against the harsh tropical sun. As they moved into different parts of the world, they were forced to adapt to different climatic conditions. Scientists believe that paler skin colour is a consequence of the long European winters and lack of strong sunlight experienced by *Homo erectus* migrants from Africa. Over thousands of years the diminished threat of ultraviolet damage would have caused the skins of those living in these areas to become lighter.

The consensus among geneticists is that racial differences between people probably arose only about 35 000 years ago.

The fact that white skin developed later than black skin does not mean that white-skinned people are more advanced. White skin merely contains less melanin as a result of having had to adapt to the northern climes. In fact, white-skinned people living in equatorial regions and in the southern hemisphere are distinctly disadvantaged in that they are more susceptible to skin cancer than darker-skinned people, whose skins contain more melanin.

Any behavioural differences between ethnic groups are thus merely a function of culture and geography, and not of biology.

The mineral worth of the region was highlighted by the discovery of gold, which in turn brought fortune seekers in their thousands to the richness of the Reef. As the Gauteng economy boomed, so did the demand for food, and modern farming became entrenched.

The Cradle of Humankind has been a theatre for human drama from the earliest times, witnessing cycles of peace and conflict as people utilized the rich resources of the land in their struggle for survival and wealth.

THE LATER STONE AGE: THE SAN

The people who can best lay claim to being the first contemporary South Africans are the San, whose ancestors were our last living link with the Later Stone Age. The San are the descendants of the original hunter-gatherers who occupied areas in and around the Cradle of Humankind for thousands of years before the arrival of Iron Age migrants from the north, who brought with them a more settled lifestyle.

Their legacy remains in the form of rock art and microlithic stone tools and other artefacts found at occupation sites. The San embodied the Later Stone Age, which lasted from about 10 000 years ago until 1 000 years ago, after which it was disrupted by the Iron Age, which overshadowed the hunter-gatherer economy.

The San refined stone tool technology to its peak, specializing in sharp-edged stone blades, the most common components of their 'tool kits'. They were also responsible for other innovations that augmented their nomadic lifestyle. Sophisticated hunters, with a deep understanding of their landscape, the San developed an in-depth knowledge of animal behaviour and the use of plants for food, medicine and poison. They hunted antelope with bows and poison-tipped arrows and dug up roots and tubers with digging sticks weighted with bored stones. They polished animal bone into needles, link-shafts and arrowheads and made bodily adornments out of ostrich eggshells and bowls from tortoise shells.

A San hunter – humanity's last living link to the Stone Age. (G)

Their root language, !Kwi, has a vast diversity of dialects, which suggests that it is an exceptionally old language and that each San hunter-gatherer group occupied a relatively small territorial range. The early relationship between the San and the Khoekhoe (Later Stone Age herders) remains unclear. They have often been lumped together as the Khoisan, but this overlooks their vastly different cultural and linguistic traditions.

ROCK ART AND TRANCE DANCE

Rock engraving of a rhino from the Magaliesberg. (RARI)

San rock art consists of a broad range of beautifully crafted symbolic images in a number of different styles, and it has given rise to an intense debate about the cosmology motivating the artists, many of whom are believed to have been shamans.

Prevailing views on San rock art assume that the paintings are of a shamanistic nature and that they are connected to trance dance rituals that invoked contact between the living and the world of the spirits. The object of the dancing, in which the whole community would be involved, was to harness the potency (N/um) bestowed by the spirit world in order to heal the sick, call for rain or bring good fortune in hunting. San shamans entered an altered state of consciousness through prolonged, rhythmic dancing and singing, intense concentration and hyperventilation.

Most of the surviving San art in the vicinity of the Cradle of Humankind consists of engravings rather than paintings, all of which are located in the Magaliesberg range to the north and west of the Cradle. From 1971, over the course of 16 years, archaeologist Robbie Steel mapped over 500 engravings in the Magaliesberg area in a personal campaign to save the art and to persuade local inhabitants to preserve and respect the images.

Most of the engravings are of identifiable animals, such as zebra and eland, superimposed with fine and irregular linear motifs that may be interpreted as ritualistic symbolism. The artists appear to have been motivated by the desire to depict beautiful or powerful images and most of the work is imbued with a deep respect for the animals depicted. Generally, the engravings were etched on fine-grained diabase rock on open, south-facing slopes.

There are only two or three notable rock art painting sites in the area. Animals that occur in the paintings include eland, one of the largest African antelopes. The eland had a special place in San cosmology, possibly because it carried more fat than most other animals and therefore played a central role in rituals.

Many of the engravings from the Magaliesberg area have been removed for safekeeping and may be viewed at the Rock Art Research Institute at the University of the Witwatersrand.

The San's most enduring legacy is their art, which has made southern Africa the world's biggest outdoor art gallery. Tens of thousands of rock paintings and engravings have been found in rock shelters and overhangs in a broad swathe from the Cape to Tanzania. The oldest of these, the Apollo 11 shelter in Namibia, has been dated to 27 500 years ago. Most existing rock art, however, was created in the last 3 000 years.

Pieces of string and stone tools dating back some 7 000 years were found by archaeologist Revil Mason at Kruger Cave between the Cradle and Rustenburg. The cave also contained paintings of more recent antiquity. San artefacts have also been discovered in the Cradle itself at Uitkomst Cave in the John Nash Nature Reserve.

EARLY IRON AGE AGROPASTORALISTS

About 2 000 years ago southern African society underwent a radical change. The centuries-old hunter-gatherer lifestyle was challenged by the arrival of migrants from the north, who brought with them new sets of ideologies and belief systems. Two discernible groups of migrants have been identified – the Khoekhoe, who were nomadic herders and hunters, and Bantu-speakers, whose impact was far more significant because they brought with them agriculture and iron-making skills.

Explaining the term 'Bantu'

The term 'Bantu' is used here in its descriptive sense, referring to a linguistic rootstock that appears to have originated in western Central Africa. The southern Bantu consist of the major language groupings of the Nguni (Zulu and Xhosa), the Tsonga, the Sotho/Tswana and the Shona. During white minority rule in South Africa, the term 'Bantu' acquired a negative connotation and was used to denote inferiority. It is, in fact, anything but that as it describes a rich and proud linguistic heritage that binds together as many as 180 million people in sub-Saharan Africa. Some academics believe, however, that the term 'SiNtu' should replace 'Bantu' because of the latter's apartheid connotations.

Exactly when the Khoekhoe arrived in South Africa is difficult to ascertain, as elements of their culture – goats, sheep and pottery – may have preceded them through trade exchanges with the San. Various archaeologists have dated their presence in the subcontinent at any time between 50 AD and 1000 AD, but what does seem clear is that by the time the first European settlers arrived in the 15th century the Khoekhoe and San appeared to retain distinct identities even though there had been some cultural and linguistic intermingling.

There is less confusion about the timing of the arrival of Bantu-speakers, whose linguistic origins lay in the tropical forests of West Africa. Their expansion into southern Africa was probably the result of political dynamics associated with burgeoning populations, and has been dated to approximately 200 AD. Their arrival is significant in that this marks the beginning of the development of the identity of the majority of modern-day South Africans.

The relationship between these early Bantu-speakers and hunter-gatherers was a complicated and varied one, partly conflictory as they competed for the same resources, and partly collaborative as they traded material goods and entered cultural exchanges. Essentially, the Bantu-speakers imposed their dominance, settling in the most watered valleys and habitable areas, forcing the San either to retreat to drier, more marginal areas to continue their hunter-gatherer lifestyles, or being absorbed as artisans, hunters or herders.

Modern-day pastoralists. (G)

The Early Iron Age economy revolved around the day-to-day production of carbohydrates through the cultivation of sorghum and millet. Settlement patterns were dictated by climatic conditions suitable for these crops – generally the summer rainfall areas of the interior. Included in their 'cultural package' was the farming of livestock and smelting and forging.

In the Cradle of Humankind area, the first Bantu-speaking settlements have been dated to approximately 500 AD and are to be found around Broederstroom. Excavations have revealed settlements comprising residential huts surrounding a central cattle area, while grain was stored in raised huts and in underground pits. Iron weapons and agricultural implements have been recovered as well as copper artefacts and decorative beads, implying that there was trade with other communities.

The remains of pottery are similar to those found in KwaZulu-Natal and East Africa, which may indicate the migration routes of these Early Iron Age settlers. Later Stone Age tools have also been found at the Early Iron Age sites at Broederstroom.

LATER IRON AGE MIGRANTS

The Iron Age economy in Africa led to a rapid population increase as food sources became more productive. This resulted in the southwards expansion of Bantu-speaking groups during the early part of the second millennium. Early Nguni speakers were probably present in KwaZulu-Natal by the 12th century AD, while the first Sotho/Tswana speakers appear in northern South Africa around 1350 AD.

Linguistically both these groups can be traced back to East Africa and this is reinforced by similarities in ceramic styles, suggesting the southwards population occurred down the continent's east coast.

Although the Later Iron Age represents more of an elaboration of, rather than a break from the Early Iron Age, the Sotho/Tswana speakers who settled in the Cradle of Humankind area between 1450 and 1500 brought with them a distinct new cultural identity. Undoubtedly there was some genetic continuity with Early Iron Age people but for the first time there is a recognizable Sotho/Tswana tradition that can be directly linked to the majority of the people in the area today. The remains of their homesteads are found in much of North West Province, Gauteng, the Free State and along the Mpumulanga escarpment. These settlements generally followed the Early Iron Age homestead layout with residential and food storage zones arranged around a central cattle byre, indicating the significance of cattle in Iron Age society.

Smelting and forging

The production of Iron Age implements required two processes – smelting and forging. Smelting involved heating iron ore in furnaces, a chemical process in which the oxygen was burnt off the iron oxides to create crude iron. Bellows made from goatskins and fitted with a cow horn nozzle were used to maintain the heat within the furnaces. Smelting was traditionally a male activity performed away from the homestead. Forging was the technique of heating crude iron into a malleable state, then beating it into implements, such as hoe heads, assegaai blades, knives and razors.

When the first European settlers established a full-time presence in Cape Town in 1652 to service ships passing from Europe to the Far East, the Iron Age settlements of the interior were expanding rapidly. Settlers first heard about these Sotho/Tswana groupings from the Nama in 1661, who spoke of them as the Thlaping or 'goat people', metal traders from the northern part of the South African interior.

A Later Iron Age stone wall enclosure in the Cradle. (IJ)

In 1801 the first reported contact took place between the Thlaping and an expedition of European explorers and missionaries who had made their way into the interior. They reported that the Thlaping, whose menfolk wore decorated knives in sheaths around their necks, were living in communities with populations larger than that of Cape Town at the time. This expedition was 'disconcerted to find that Thlaping knives were preferred to the trade knives offered' (Wilson, 1969) and that the products of Kaditshwene (which was some 200 kilometres west of the Cradle of Humankind) were equal to any steel known to the Europeans.

As colonial frontiers expanded during the 19th century, the Sotho/Tswana groupings on the highveld became part of a broader trading community. This led to greater wealth, but also increased competition – not only in trading terms but also in access to natural resources. These tensions were the seeds of future conflict, as hostility grew with the marginalized San, who were primarily blamed for widespread cattle theft, and within various lineages of the Sotho/Tswana groupings as well as with the Griqua of the southwest.

In the early 1820s John Campbell visited Kaditshwene and reported that there were more than 16 000 people living in thousands of painted huts grouped together and protected by stone walls. Campbell and the missionary Robert Moffat, on their travels in the vicinity of what is today Rustenburg, also came across settlements such as Molokwane and Boitsemegano, populated by up to 15 000 people. These settlements had flourished as a result of economies based on mixed agriculture and commerce. Little did they know that they were witnessing the Iron Age at its peak, and that 500 years of relative social stability were about to be destroyed.

UITKOMST CAVE

Uitkomst Cave, situated in the John Nash Nature Reserve, provides a glimpse of the transition from the Later Stone Age to the Iron Ages. It appears to have been inhabited on and off for at least 10 000 years.

Uitkomst was discovered by archaeologist Revil Mason during the early sixties and was chosen as a 'type' site for Sotho/Tswana pottery that was also found at four other Iron Age sites in the broad ambit of the Cradle of Humankind – at Glenferness, Hennops River, Pietkloof and Zwartkops.

Uitkomst is important for two main reasons:

- it contains evidence of the Later Stone Age and the Iron Ages;
- the variety of artefacts found, including distinctive Sotho/Tswana pottery, smelting furnaces and debris that is associated with dry stone wall building.

The Later Stone Age remains from Uitkomst occur in the deposit just above the bedrock. The remains of a fire hearth have been discovered, where presumably hunter-gatherers roasted meat and huddled together against the winter cold. A number of scrapers and microlithic tools are associated with this early deposit, known as Bed 1.

The main Iron Age artefacts are two crude iron furnaces dating back approximately 500 years and a more refined 'modern' smelter built over the remains of one of the earlier ones. The early furnaces had single nozzles through which air was pumped into the melting chamber by means of bellows to maintain the heat, whereas the later furnace had two nozzles, presumably to prolong the smelting process.

Diagnostic Uitkomst pottery pattern.

The more recent furnace was thickly coated with slag, which suggests it was used for a long period. V-shaped wooden tools were used to extract the iron from the furnaces. Traces of copper and iron have been recovered from both furnaces. The remains of copper bracelets have been found at the site, and are thought to have been produced by Later Iron Age metal workers. Analysis of the stratigraphy suggests that the Uitkomst Cave was first used as a smelting centre and then, towards the end of the Iron Age, as a dwelling.

Uitkomst pottery is an important chronological indicator in that the dozens of recovered sherds have diagnostic rims, most of which are plain, although some are ornately stamped and incised. The bowls were fairly deep, with a rim diameter of about 12 cm, and all appear to have been carefully made and well fired. There is a cohesion in their style and execution that suggests that one main pottery tradition occupied the central part of Gauteng and the northern Free State during the Later Iron Age.

Uitkomst Cave. (IJ)

Two stone walls were built around the Uitkomst shelter. Their style of construction is associated with the style of the pottery, reinforcing the theory that a single overarching Iron Age culture was rooted in the Cradle of Humankind. Other artefacts from Uitkomst tell us more about the Iron Age way of life. The remains of reed mats held together by fibre strings appear to have been the beds that people slept on. They made rope of grass or vegetable fibre, they ate off skilfully carved wooden bowls, drank beer and other beverages from clay pots and used grindstones to refine sorghum for food preparation. They wore shell pendants, probably garnered in trade with the eastern coast.

Mason, whose study of the Uitkomst Cave was published in his *Prehistory of the Transvaal*, concludes that Uitkomst people knew how to 'extract a surprising amount from their environment, considering their limited technology. They turned shapeless clay into good pottery, sought out small mineralized lodes and extracted copper ore, moulded mud into furnaces, twisted grass or root fibres into a variety of complex strings and ropes for tying bundles, kept domestic cattle and cultivated crops. The single cowrie shell indicates that some contact with the east coast was established but there is no other sign of trade or coastal contact' (1962:395). The Uitkomst people were the ancestors of the BaFokeng who today occupy the platinum-rich area near Sun City to the west of the Cradle of Humankind.

CATTLE AS CURRENCY

The importance of cattle in indigenous society has its roots in the Iron Age. Although it is unclear how cattle were introduced into South Africa, the Bantu-speaking migrants of the Early Iron Age definitely possessed cows. Their presence marked a shift in the primitive economy towards wealth creation rather than mere subsistence. The first recorded appearance of cattle in southern Africa dates back to the 5th century, although these animals had already been part of a North African culture for thousands of years (from about 4 500 BCE).

Cattle were valued not only as a source of milk and meat, but were a store of value and a symbol of power. By the Later Iron Age, cattle had become a key part of the social dynamics of Bantu-speaking communities. Indeed some historians have suggested that Sotho/Tswana societies developed on the basis of royal control of cattle through the mafisa system, as well as through the profits of mining and trading. Mafisa cattle were livestock loaned by chiefs to their subjects in return for allegiance and support. Along with the lobola system – a marriage payment made by the family of the husband to that of the wife – the mafisa is one of the few Iron Age customs that survives in certain rural areas of modern southern Africa.

Architectural styles of Later Iron Age settlements reflect the significance of cattle, which were kept in the middle of communal villages. Archaeologists have described this social dynamic as the Central Cattle Pattern, which was prevalent not only in the Sotho/Tswana communities of the highveld, but among Nguni speakers of the eastern coastal plains. Important social figures were often buried beneath these central cattle byres.

Of war and peace

One of the myths about southern Africa is that its people have always been at war with each other. This is not the case. For hundreds of years there were periods of relative peace and stability when people of different cultures interacted without violence.

The Sotho/Tswana societies that occupied the region around the Cradle of Humankind had tolerant political and social systems, based on a democratic rather than an autocratic style of government, with many decisions being taken by a pitso, or general assembly, rather than by a chief. The missionary John Philip noted in 1820 how free men were able to criticize a Tswana chief and that, under Tswana law, a chief could be tried and fined by his own counsellors.

Interestingly, it was probably this culture of political tolerance that made the Sotho/Tswana societies so vulnerable to the invasion of a relatively small military force of Nguni-speakers under Mzilikazi, who ultimately remoulded the political landscape of Iron Age Sotho/Tswana culture, bringing it under his military control by the 1830s.

An aerial view of the circular ruins of Molokwane, near the Cradle of Humankind. (TH)

THE END OF THE IRON AGES

During the 1820s, the competition within Sotho/Tswana society for trading influence and natural resources exploded into inter-community violence. This heralded the 'Difaqane' (Sotho for 'the time of conflict'). This was a separate dynamic from the 'Mfeqane' (Zulu for 'the crushing') which coincided with the rise to power of the Zulu king Shaka, whose military consolidation of clans around him sparked off a series of local conflicts in what is today KwaZulu-Natal. Although the relationship between the Difaqane and the Mfeqane remains a subject of historical speculation, these dynamics affected vast areas of the subcontinent, with thousands of people losing their lives or being displaced and impoverished as a result.

This period of instability was significant, not only in the way that it reshaped indigenous societies geographically and politically, but in the way that it opened up the interior for white settler expansion. In the aftermath of the Mfeqane and the Difaqane, when the Voortrekkers and other white settlers moved into the interior, they found it relatively easy to lay claim to large tracts of agriculturally suitable land as their own, because indigenous societies had been so weakened by the turmoil.

LIFE AND WATER

The settlement patterns of Iron Age people such as the Sotho/Tswana and Nguni were determined largely by the environment. The key factor in this regard was obviously the availability of water. Water therefore had a direct influence on the culture and belief systems that developed in the Iron Age.

The rolling grasslands of the broader ecosystem in which the Cradle of Humankind is situated (the Gauteng and Free State highveld) were not as well watered as the subtropical foothills and valleys of KwaZulu-Natal and the Eastern Cape, which were settled by the Nguni. Rain was therefore much more important to the Sotho/Tswana, and is reflected as such in their cosmology.

Death and danger were associated with heat. The ancient Sotho/Tswana healing rituals were therefore based on cooling. Four substances were generally used to achieve a cooling effect, namely water, chyme (the partially digested stomach contents of an animal), cold ash and used charcoal (the coolness that replaces fire when it has burnt itself out).

The Nguni view of danger and evil was associated with darkness and dirt. Thus their healing systems were based on the need to purge the body, either through enemas or vomiting.

The social structures of Sotho/Tswana and Nguni societies were also influenced by the availability of water. Autonomous clusters of homesteads were the dominant social structure in Nguni culture, because they could be self-sustaining. On the highveld there were far greater concentrations of people close to water sources and therefore decision-making was very centralized.

A spring in the John Nash Nature Reserve. (IJ)

A vista of the Magaliesberg from the Cradle. (IJ)

IN 1829 THE MISSIONARY MOFFAT DESCRIBED WHAT HE SAW IN THE MAGALIESBERG AND CRADLE OF HUMANKIND AREA:

'. . . the ruins of innumerable towns, some of amazing extent . . . They exhibited signs of immense labor . . . every fence being composed of stones . . . averaging five or six feet high. Some of the houses which escaped the flames of marauders were large and showed a far superior style and taste to anything I had before witnessed . . . The whole country appeared once to contain a dense population. Now since the invasion . . . and the terror . . . it had become the habitation of wild beasts.'

It appears that the first Mfeqane foray into the Cradle of Humankind area took place in 1827. This was an invasion by Mzilikazi and his formidable force of Nguni-speakers who, having fled the wrath of Shaka, moved northwards over the Vaal River. Although his army was relatively small, it appeared to be well disciplined, and Mzilikazi moved swiftly across the grasslands of the Cradle of Humankind, into the Magaliesberg, plundering and destroying every settlement he came across. His success was made easier by the fact that the Sotho/Tswana groupings in his path had been considerably weakened by the preceding Difaqane. This had taken the form of at least five years of internal strife in a series of conflicts between the Pedi, Po, Kwena and BaFokeng clans, which marked the end of centuries of

The Mfeqane put an end to the relatively peaceful era of the Later Iron Age. (MA)

relative peace and prosperity that had characterized the Iron Ages. His conquest of the Sotho/Tswana now complete, Mzilikazi established himself at the foot of the Wonderboom Mountain near present-day Pretoria, where he founded his capital, Kungwini. He also built a residence, Dinaneno, near Hartbeespoort Dam just north of the Cradle. Direct evidence of the trauma of these times can still be found today in caves such as Gladysvale, where dung floors deep in the interior of the caves bear witness to how people used to hide cattle, their most prized possessions, from marauders.

From 1827 to about 1837, Mzilikazi ruled a substantial area of what is today North West Province, Northern Province and Gauteng. He established a series of settlements run on regimental lines and his Ndebele army ruled the conquered Sotho/Tswana population. Mzilikazi's kingdom encroached on the territory of the Griqua and Korana frontiersmen, who lived in what is today the Northern Cape. Over the next three years these frontiersmen mounted a number of raids on Mzilikazi, but he finally quelled them in a decisive battle near the village of Bospoort in the mountains to the west of the Cradle. Mzilikazi was also attacked by Zulu raiding parties from the south under the command of Shaka's brother, Dingane, and responded by moving his capital west of the Magaliesberg to the present-day town of Zeerust.

MOGALE

The Magaliesberg range of mountains and valleys to the north and west of the Cradle was named after Chief Mogale Mogale, a prominent leader of the Po tribe that inhabited the Magaliesberg at the time of the Mfeqane. Krugersdorp was renamed Mogale City in his honour.

As a youngster Mogale survived an invasion by the Pedi in 1823, when his grandparents hid him in the bush during raids for cattle, women and children. When Mzilikazi attacked the Po five years later, they captured Mogale as the tribe fled into the surrounding foothills. However, a group of Po returned in a brave surprise attack and rescued the young man, who soon became their leader. One of his first acts was to regroup the Po and lead them southwards across the Vaal to a safer place. When the Boers arrived and established themselves in the area in the 1830s, Mogale negotiated a deal with them and, in a joint military operation, drove out the Ndebele who had settled on the Po's lands in the Magaliesberg Valley. In 1845 the president of the newly formed Transvaal Republic, Paul Kruger, sent his brother Gert to administer the area comprising the Cradle of Humankind and the Magaliesberg. It appears that Gert named the Magaliesberg after Mogale in recognition of his assistance in defeating the Ndebele. Nonetheless, as natural history writer Vincent Carruthers pointed out in his book on the Magaliesberg (2000:264): 'The naming provided little benefit to the chief of the Po, for his lands were ploughed and planted by the Boers and his people were put to work digging irrigation furrows from the river, which was also given his name.'

Chief Mogale Mogale.

Chief Mogale naturally resented this subjugation and resisted the Boers. In 1847 he was suspected by the Transvaal authorities of gunrunning and conspiring to overthrow the government. Seeing the writing on the wall, Mogale fled with a number of his followers to Thaba Nchu in the Free State. Some 15 years later he made peace with the then president of the Transvaal, Marthinus Pretorius, and in 1863 the Po repurchased their sacred lands in the Magaliesberg area, where some of their descendants still live today.

THE VOORTREKKERS

Mzilikazi was finally overthrown by a new group of immigrants, the Voortrekkers. From 1836 onwards, these bands of Dutch settlers moved into the interior of the country, dissatisfied with the British administration that ruled the Cape.

The vast stretches of 'uninhabited' land they came across were an accident of their immediate history. The wake of the terrible Mfeqane had left vast areas deserted and led to the widespread myth that the interior was, and had been, unoccupied by indigenous people and thus could be rightfully claimed by the Boers. They set up farms in the area and developed the land for European agricultural practices.

In 1836 Mzilikazi's forces ambushed a Boer hunting party under Stephanus Erasmus to the north of the Cradle. All but three of its members were killed. This precipitated a series of skirmishes between the Dutch settlers and the Ndebele, culminating in the battle of Vegkop, where 40 Boer families managed to withstand an attack by 3 000 Ndebele tribesmen. This defeat greatly weakened Mzilikazi's fighting force and his reputation. His traditional enemies, the Zulu, swept through the Magaliesberg in 1837 and took on Mzilikazi in a battle in the Pilanesberg, close to where Sun City stands today.

Mzilikazi fled north across the Limpopo and re-established his capital at Bulawayo in present-day Zimbabwe. His departure opened up the way for the Dutch settlers to take

Journeys into the interior

The early 1800s were a volatile time in southern Africa, characterized by a number of population migrations due to a variety of economic and political circumstances. There was widespread social upheaval because of the consolidation of Zulu power in KwaZulu-Natal, commonly referred to as the Mfeqane. Tswana/Sotho communities of the highveld were drawn into conflict and population displacement by competition over natural resources and political rivalry. And Britain's tightening grip over the Cape Colony led to the Great Trek (an exodus by the Voortrekkers of Dutch descent, who ventured into the subcontinent in a bid to maintain some form of independence from the British). The Voortrekkers eventually went on to establish the Transvaal and Free State republics.

Although the Great Trek has been hailed as a triumph of spirit over adversity – and without wanting to detract from the courage and bravery that characterized this settler migration – it was just one of many monumental journeys undertaken during the period. Indeed, what was probably the longest, most arduous trek of the time was that undertaken by the Ngoni clan who left KwaZulu-Natal during the Mfeqane. Under the chieftainship of Zwangendaba, they travelled 1 600 kilometres through present-day Zimbabwe and Zambia before eventually settling in what is now Tanzania.

control of the territory following the Great Trek of 1838, which saw increasing numbers of disaffected Boers leaving the Cape and Natal to establish what eventually became the Transvaal and Free State republics.

With the defeat of Mzilikazi by the Boers, and the British having pacified the Zulu through a series of campaigns in the 1820s and 1830s, the rest of the 19th century saw a battle for political dominance between these two groups. The Boers negotiated their independence from the British in 1852, and in 1855 the Afrikaner capital of Pretoria was established, named after the Voortrekker leader Andries Pretorius. However, ongoing acrimony over the terms of independence continued between the two groups, resulting in the British decision to annex the Transvaal in 1877.

In 1880, 4 000 Boers met just southwest of the Cradle at Paardekraal, near Mogale City (Krugersdorp), to protest against British rule, and under the leadership of Paul Kruger proclaimed the independence of the South African Republic. This led to the first South African War (previously known as the First Boer War), which ended three years later with the defeat of the British and the reinstatement of Afrikaner sovereignty.

THE DISCOVERY OF GOLD

A new development occurred during the 1880s that was to change the face of South Africa and the balance of political power. Gold was discovered on a farm called Langlaagte, 50 kilometres to the south of the Cradle on the Witwatersrand ridge. The mining village that would become Johannesburg, named after Johann Rissik and Christian Johannes Joubert, was laid out in 1886 after thousands of fortune seekers descended on the area in the hope of finding riches beyond their dreams. Most of those dreams ended in disappointment, but a few did strike it lucky.

In a renewal of hostilities between Boer and British, ultimately over control of the gold fields, war broke out again in 1899. The Magaliesberg area was an important arena in the second South African War (also known as the Second Boer War) and many battles were fought in the mountain range, which served as a base for many of the Boer commandos. One of the British blockhouses, nicknamed Barton's Folly, still survives outside Hekpoort just beyond Mogale's Gate.

From the Magaliesberg, Boer generals such as De la Rey, De Wet, Smuts and Kemp led regular sorties against the British, who were particularly ruthless in suppressing the Boer population. Many farms were destroyed as a result of the British 'scorched earth' policy and countless Boer women and children, as well as black civilians, were incarcerated in the notorious British concentration camps.

A scene from early Johannesburg in the late 1800s. *(MA)*

Tensions between English- and Afrikaans-speaking white South Africans continued well beyond the end of the South African War, and dominated the politics of the early 20th century. Where the English- and Afrikaans-speaking white South Africans were generally united, however, was in their notion of white superiority, an attitude that resulted in the founding of the African National Congress in 1912, the primary organization representing black political aspirations. The second half of the 20th century came to be dominated by the politics of black resistance to white domination, resulting in South Africa's eventual transformation into a fully democratic society in 1994.

This relatively peaceful shift in power has often been ascribed to South Africa's prosperity, in which the gold industry has played a major part. This leads to what is a rather spurious observation regarding the history of the Cradle of Humankind and its environs: there has been a deep thread of continuity in the relationship between the people who have lived there and its geology. From the preservation of the fossils of some of our earliest ancestors to the fashioning of stone tools by early *Homo*, from the furnaces of the Iron Ages to the discovery of gold, the occupants of the area have – to a greater or lesser extent – depended on the mineral qualities of the rocks around and below them for their livelihood.

THE BATTLE OF DWARSVLEI

The battle of Dwarsvlei took place at the edge of the Cradle on 11 July 1900. A force of 1 300 Gordon Highlanders commanded by Major General HA Smith-Dorrien marched from Krugersdorp towards Hekpoort to link up with other units to relieve the siege of Rustenburg. Fifteen kilometres north of Krugersdorp the road rises steeply towards Daspoortrand. There, some 750 Boer commandos under Sarel Oosthuizen opened fire on the British. The British artillery was drawn up on an exposed hill west of the road and opened fire. The Boers, however, got to a closer ridge and unleashed deadly fire on the gunners, killing their horses. Only three of the sixteen gunners survived the repeated charges by the Boers, who captured most of the wagons and supplies destined for Rustenburg. Smith-Dorrien, expecting reinforcements to arrive, was unaware that the Royal Artillery and the Scots Greys cavalry under Lieutenant Colonel WP Alexander had been attacked by the Boers that same day at Silkaatsnek north of the Hartbeespoort Dam, and were unable to come to their assistance. Severe casualties were suffered on both sides, including Oosthuizen, who died during a charge against the artillery. Two Victoria Crosses were awarded, to Captain WE Gordon and Captain DR Younger. The British managed to extricate their guns and some of their wagons and retreated to Krugersdorp. It was a victory for the Boers despite their casualties, as the line of communication between the Witwatersrand and Rustenburg was sealed off.

(SA)

THE LIVING LANDSCAPE

The Cradle of Humankind, as well as the surrounding landscape, is one of the storehouses of the planet's wealth. The mineral deposits exploited by Iron Age societies were just the tip of the proverbial iceberg. It is only in the last century that the full extent of the mineral deposits of the area – and their value – has been revealed.

Over half the world's total gold supply – some 45 000 tons – originated in the three-billion-year-old rocks of the Witwatersrand, just south of the Cradle of Humankind. Further to the west are some of the world's richest platinum mines.

These riches are a consequence of the Earth being in a continual state of flux. Throughout the planet's 4,2-billion-year history, landmasses have moved around in an ongoing, imperceptibly slow-motion geological drama, changing the shape and position of the continents.

THE WITWATERSRAND BASIN

Three billion years ago the Cradle of Humankind was part of a large inland sea situated over the equator. This huge basin, which covered what is now southern Gauteng and the northern Free State, lay over a relatively stable part of the Earth's crust, the Kaapvaal Craton.

Surrounding this sea was a range of very high granite domes. Over time these mountains eroded, depositing their sediments in the relatively shallow waters of a continental shelf and low-lying coastal plains. As this erosion process continued, pebbles, sand and mud, along with minerals such as gold and uranium, were washed into the deeper parts of the lake, eventually creating a 7,5 km deep layer of primal rubble on the floor of the basin.

The centre of the basin subsided and the weight of the overlying material compacted the original mud, sand and pebbles into hard rocks known respectively as shale, quartzite and conglomerate. These rocks, collectively known as the Witwatersrand Super Group, are exposed in the ridge that runs from the town of Springs to the town of Randfontein and continue further westwards to Klerksdorp and on into the northern Free State, where they lie under layers of younger Karoo-aged rocks.

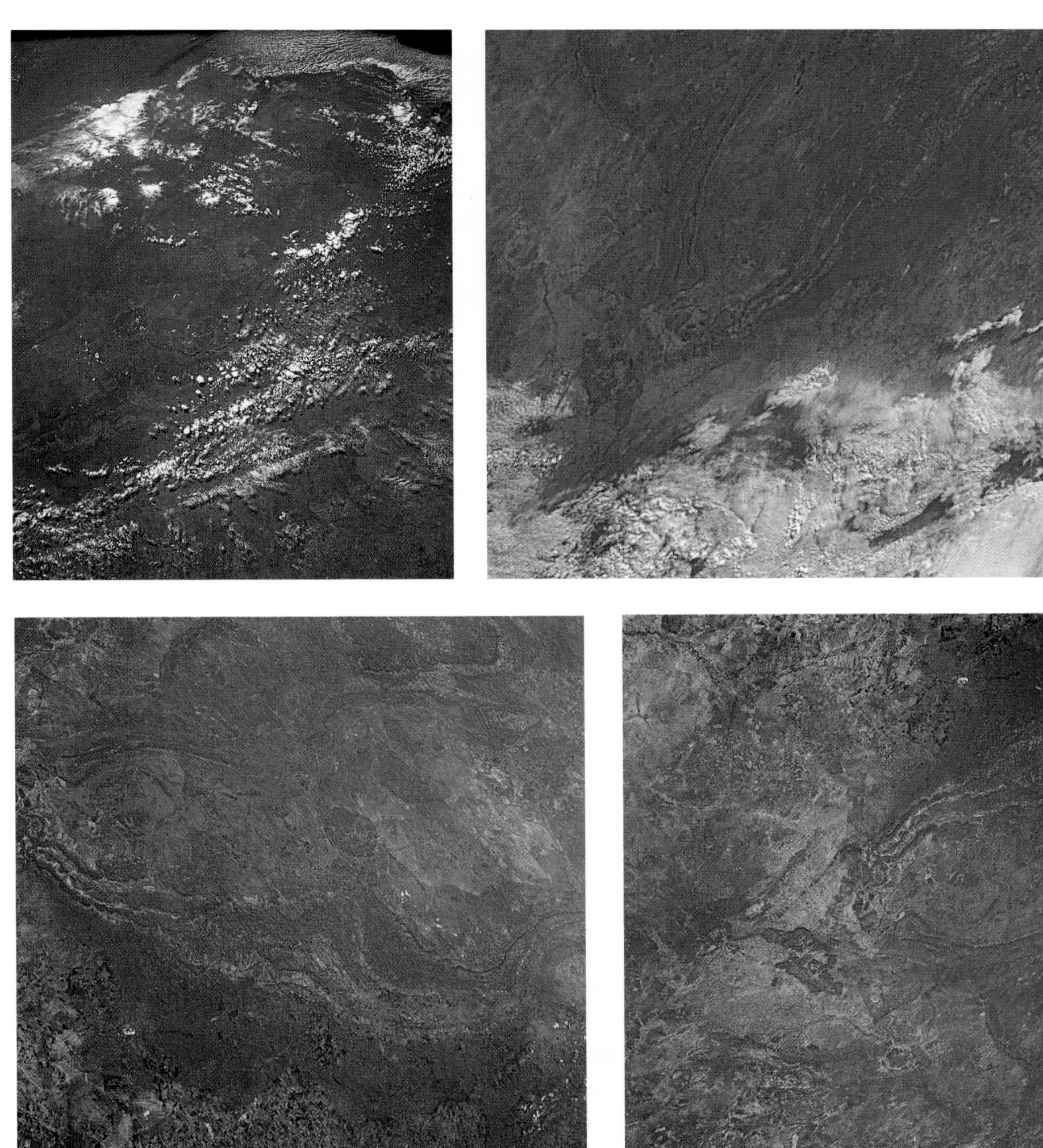

The Witwatersrand as seen from space, taken from (top left) the space shuttle Discovery *with an AeroLinhof large-format camera, (top right) the space shuttle* Atlantis *with a 70 mm hand-held Hasselblad camera, and (bottom left and right) from the space shuttle* Challenger *with a 70 mm hand-held Hasselblad camera.* (NASA)

GOLD ON THE WITWATERSRAND

Liquid gold being poured into a mould. (SIL)

The first hint that gold might shape the future of the Witwatersrand was the discovery of gold-bearing ore in the Cradle of Humankind in 1874. Traces of the metal were found along the Blaauwbank stream, but the find proved frustratingly insubstantial.

Only in 1881 was a significant find made, when prospector Johannes Stephanus Minnaar came across a gold nugget on the farm Kromdraai. Further exploration led to the discovery of the Kromdraai Reef later that year. When this was brought to the attention of the farm owner, JH Grobelaar, he quickly applied for the mineral rights to the land and was granted a concession of about 100 hectares. The rest of the farm was declared a public digging. A considerable number of fortune seekers tried their luck at panning for gold and some were very successful. Within a few years, the Kromdraai Gold Mining Company was formed, publishing its prospectus in the *Volkstem* newspaper in 1886.

By this time Johannesburg was in a gold frenzy. Gold had been discovered on the farm Langlaagte on the site of present-day Johannesburg by George Walker and George Harrison. This prompted one of the world's biggest gold rushes as thousands of people from around the world made their way to the site. Scores of small mines sprang up literally overnight as fortune seekers mined the surface deposits of the reef in a shallow series of workings and incline shafts. The activity attracted the interest of the fledgling finance houses that had emerged from the Kimberley diamond rush and they funded a variety of land-buying syndicates which then set about raising finance for serious mining operations. Johannesburg was proclaimed – named after the two Transvaal Republic commissioners responsible for the area – Johann Rissik and Christian Johannes Joubert. Johannesburg soon became the powerhouse of the South African economy, a position it holds today as the centre of Gauteng province (Sotho for 'the place of gold').

The Kromdraai mine itself was relatively short-lived. It produced its first gold in 1887, when just over two kilograms of the metal were extracted from 270 kilograms of quartz using a stamp battery erected at the confluence of the Blaauwbank stream and the Crocodile River. The mine was discontinued in 1912 when it became clear that its gold reserves were unsustainable.

The Kromdraai gold mine. (IJ)

A view of the Black Reef near the Kromdraai road. (IJ)

The quartzites, made up mainly of the mineral quartz, are the most resistant to weathering and therefore usually form the ridges, like the Swartkoppies hill at the southern edge of the Cradle of Humankind, while the softer shales are eroded more easily and tend to occupy the valley floors. The conglomerates, in which gold and other precious metals are found, occur in thin bands or reefs that run through the area.

One of the more unusual reefs that breaks the surface in the Cradle of Humankind is the so-called Black Reef, which can be viewed along the Kromdraai road that winds past some of the earliest subsurface gold mines in South Africa. The Kromdraai road also marks a change in the geology of the Cradle. To the south are the Witwatersrand rocks and to the north are the stromatolite-rich dolomitic rocks of the Monte Cristo and Eccles formations.

STROMATOLITES

Beyond 2 billion years ago, the oxygen levels in the planet's atmosphere were too low to support life as we know it. The dominant form of life on Earth then was algae, unicellular and multicellular plants that lack stems, roots and leaves and grow in moist areas. Over millions of years the photosynthesizing actions of algae, in which carbon dioxide is transformed into oxygen, probably raised the oxygen levels in the atmosphere to a point where oxygen-dependent life forms could evolve.

Fossilized stromatolites in the Cradle of Humankind. (IJ)

Stromatolites are fossilized colonies of algae, appearing as dome-shaped or arched rocks in the extensive exposures of dolomitic rock that occur in the Chuniespoort Group. The volcanic ash layers in these rocks have been dated to between 2,4 and 2,6 billion years ago.

Most of the larger stromatolites in the Cradle of Humankind are the fossilized remains of cyanobacteria colonies, better known as blue-green algae mats. The cyanobacteria grew in thin mats on the floor of the ancient ocean that once covered the Cradle of Humankind. The sticky sheaths around the algal fibres captured fine grains of calcium carbonate, which then formed layers, blocking out the sunlight from the algae. The algae responded by growing through the calcium layer, forming fine bands that over time built up into massive stromatolites.

Not all stromatolites are fossils. This picture shows living stromatolites in intertidal flats at Shark Bay, Western Australia. (NB)

The Cradle of Humankind has various sites where stromatolites can be viewed. There are particularly good colonies near Coopers, in the John Nash Nature Reserve and in the Cradle Game Reserve.

CAVE-FORMING DOLOMITES

The geological feature of most significance in terms of the preservation of early human origins is the Worldkarst, or cave-forming, dolomites that occur within the protected area. This at least 1 220 m thick layer of rock, formed at the bottom of the ancient sea beds 2,5 billion years ago, is recognizable from the way it juts out of the grassland and hilltops.

Tilted slightly northwards, the dolomites are generally inhospitable to larger trees as they do not support topsoil very well. It is only where caves have undercut an area of hard dolomite, or where streams and rivers have gouged their way into the rock and formed narrow floodplains, that larger plants can gain a foothold.

White stinkwoods and olive trees growing in a sinkhole. (IJ)

One of the ways in which scientists have identified areas in the dolomites where there may be caves is to look for the occurrence of lime-loving trees such as the Wild Olive *Olea capensis* and the White Stinkwood *Celtis africana*. Often, their presence marks the top of an underground cavity into which their roots grow.

Unfortunately, many of the magnificent stinkwoods that must have grown in the hidden valleys of the Cradle of Humankind were felled at the beginning of the 20th century to use as fuel for lime furnaces, and so only their stumps remain as clues to where potentially fossil-rich caves might be.

THE VREDEFORT IMPACT

The little Free State town of Vredefort, 200 kilometres to the south of the Cradle of Humankind, has long been a site of geological mystery. Scientists studying the area for the past hundred years are in agreement that it is the scene of some ancient geological catastrophe. The rocks are all sharply upturned, extensively fractured and fragmented. There are shatter cones and strange exposures of elongated, melted rock, all of which suggest that an event of extreme pressure took place in the distant past. Theories have abounded about whether this was caused by an ancient seismic earthquake or a meteorite strike, but it was only during the 1990s, when Wits scientist Professor Uwe Reimold launched a new investigation, that the catastrophe was conclusively proved to have been caused by an alien rock strike. The Vredefort Impact, as this feature is now called, is the largest known site of extraterrestrial impact on Earth.

Making use of the latest technology, Professor Reimold and his colleagues studied mineral deformations under a microscope and found evidence of what they called 'shock metamorphic' effects, which can only be produced at extremely high pressures (in excess of 400 kilobars). They then found tiny traces of meteoric material in the Vredefort rocks, proving beyond doubt the origin of the Vredefort Impact structure.

Imagine, if you can, the Earth in its geological adolescence, spinning through space. Its surface of rock and water is virtually lifeless because of the absence of oxygen in the atmosphere, and its molten core is still churning in a rage of gaseous consolidation from its blazing birth 2 billion years before. The planet is populated only by single-celled organisms without nuclei.

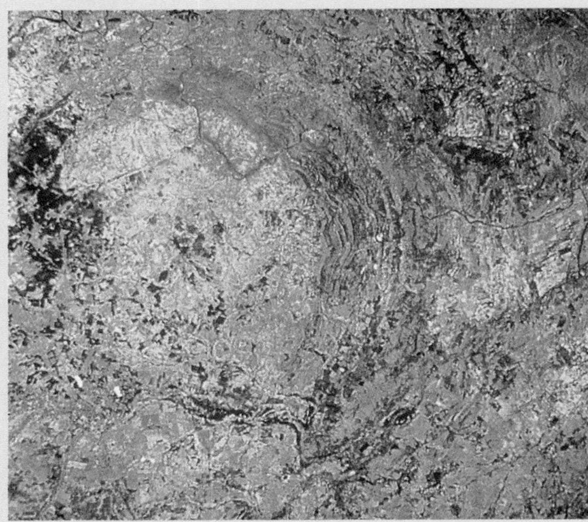

Satellite image of the Vredefort Impact area. (UR)

Then, suddenly, its orbit around the sun is violently interrupted as the globe is struck by a ten-kilometre wide meteorite at a speed of over 100 000 kilometres per hour. The resultant explosion unleashed the force of 10 million atomic bombs, gouging a smouldering 70-kilometre wide crater across the southern wastelands of the Earth. The impact may well have led to an increase in the oxygen levels of the atmosphere, which would have allowed more complicated life forms to develop, inexorably altering the destiny of this fledgling planet.

Vredefort Impact rock. (UR)

A secondary consequence of the impact was the protection it gave to the subterranean gold seams that snake in a broad arc from the northern Free State gold fields around Welkom, through Potchefstroom and the Far West Rand, to the Witwatersrand Ridge. The gold deposits, which had already been in existence for 900 million years before the Vredefort Impact, were driven deep into the Earth's surface by the meteorite collision, and thus prevented from eroding away like many other alluvial gold fields.

International visitors are able to view examples of the Vredefort granite at Johannesburg International Airport, as the pillars in the arrival hall are made from the stone and clearly show the black veins of fragmented rock produced by the impact.

For a more dramatic view of a meteorite impact, a visit to Tswaing on the northern side of the Cradle of Humankind is recommended. Tswaing is the site of a younger impact, around 200 000 years old, of a much smaller meteorite. The crater is approximately 1,1 kilometres across and is an impressive sight to behold.

Two different dolomite formations exist in the Cradle of Humankind. The dolomites in the south of the area, around Sterkfontein and the traditional fossil sites, are part of the older (2,6 to 2,8 billion years old) Monte Cristo formation, which reaches as far as Drimolen and the Rhino & Lion Nature Reserve. These rocks are flatter and more block-like than those in the northeast near the sites of Gladysvale, Motsetse and Gondolin, which are from the younger Eccles formation (2,3 to 2,5 billion years old).

Dolomites in the vicinity of Sterkfontein. (IJ)

From the surface one would never guess that within the dolomites winds a honeycomb-like network of underground caves that stretches for many kilometres. Many of these passages are under the water table and are thus not accessible without scuba gear.

One can often identify the presence of a cave beneath the surface by the trees growing in the mouth or by the presence of a sinkhole, which is caused when the ground collapses into an underlying space.

Caving opportunities abound in the area, but some routes are definitely not for the claustrophobic. For the less intrepid, the Wonder Cave is an excellent opportunity to see unmined flowstone formations and fossils in the making. The Sterkfontein underground tour offers a close-up look at a more extensive system and an underground lake, but one that has been damaged by mining. Remember that one needs permission to enter caves, and that it is illegal to collect any cave formations. It can be extremely dangerous to venture into the caves on one's own as many of them are still occupied by predators such as hyenas and leopards. These animals – along with porcupines – are the most common bone-collecting mammals in the area today, exhibiting the same behaviour as their ancestors did millions of years ago.

Inside Wonder Cave. (GG)

One of the noticeable features of the geology of the Cradle of Humankind is an orange-coloured 'topping' on some of the rocks, known as giant chert. This feature is particularly visible from the Kromdraai or Hartebeeshoek roads. There is some debate as to how old this chert is. The conventional wisdom has been that these rocks are the eroded remnants of a dinosaur-aged Cretaceous landscape 65–75 million years old. This has prompted some intrepid palaeontologists to look for dinosaur remains in these sediments. However, recent research suggests that the giant chert may be closer in age to the dolomites, which would make these rocks 2,5 billion years old. But the actual age of these rocks remains uncertain and awaits further research.

THE BREAK-UP OF GONDWANA

Everything on Earth is part of a process of change. Not even the rocks in the landscape are fixed if one looks at the planet in the context of its 4-billion-year-old history. The continents rest on geological plates that move almost imperceptibly across the surface of the Earth, changing the shape of landmasses and oceans over time.

During the Carboniferous era 320 million years ago, southern Africa lay trapped under a vast ice cap for a 50-million-year period. At that time it was part of Gondwanaland, a giant landmass that consisted of Africa, South America, Australia, Antarctica, India and Madagascar.

(CHT)

Earlier, Gondwanaland itself was linked to the northern hemisphere landmass of Laurasia. Collectively, these two landmasses formed the supercontinent Pangea. During the reign of the dinosaurs in the Jurassic Period 200 million years ago, the landmasses began to split up at a rate of between two and ten millimetres a year, until the southern and northern continents separated.

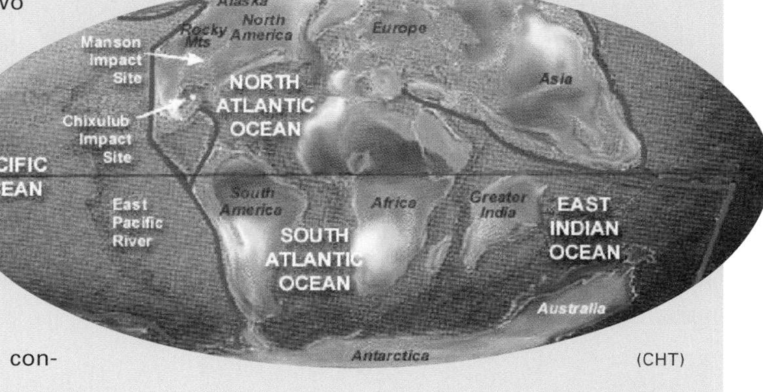

(CHT)

From approximately 120 million years ago, the African continent began its migration away from the Gondwana 'mother mass'. South America began shifting westwards, Antarctica moved to the southeast, Australia towards the east and India moved north, eventually colliding with the Asian plate.

It was only about 20 million years ago that the continents reached the point of separation that we recognize today. This also marked the beginning of our modern climate, which was influenced greatly by the oceanic currents.

Giant chert on a hill in the Cradle. (IJ)

Also scattered throughout the Cradle of Humankind are small pockets of other types of rock and minerals. A sharp-eyed amateur geologist might find outcroppings of lead, copper and umber. The many mining pits that are scattered throughout the area attest to the mineral potential that early explorers recognized in the area.

On the northern edge of the Cradle of Humankind, just south of and underneath the Hartebeeshoek road, are younger shales that are probably 2 billion years old. They are easy to recognize as they create soft, gentle slopes when they erode as opposed to the blockier, crumbly appearance of the dolomites and giant cherts. The contact point between the older dolomites and younger shales is invariably characterized by the presence of a stream or spring fountainhead. The dolomites act as aquifers, but the denser shales are less easily penetrated, so where they meet, water tends to force its way up to the surface.

If arrangements are made with a private landowner one can access abandoned shale quarries on the northern side of the Cradle of Humankind. These quarries were mined for roof shingles and floor slate and provide a remarkable glimpse of beautiful and ancient mudstones, as well as an interesting look at the type of open-pit mining that was common before more environmentally sensitive mining practices were introduced. If you are lucky, you may get to take a trip to one of the many pure springs that erupt with surprising force along the shale/dolomite contact point. A particularly good area for viewing such springs is Plover's Lake, or below the Gladysvale Cave on the John Nash Nature Reserve.

IN SEARCH OF HUMAN ORIGINS

Beneath the grasslands and dolomitic outcrops of the Cradle of Humankind lies an extensive series of underground caverns that have preserved clues of our most ancient past. For the better part of the last century, the Sterkfontein caves and surrounding fossil sites have been the focus of the southern African search for human origins.

Since Robert Broom's discovery of an adult ape-man specimen at Sterkfontein in the mid-1930s, research in the Cradle of Humankind has shaped much of our thinking about the relationship between the australopithecines and our own genus, *Homo*. Subsequent fossil finds have proved beyond doubt that humanity originated in Africa, and indeed evidence suggests that the emergence of our own species may well have occurred in South Africa.

The first recorded discovery of the Sterkfontein caves, initially known as the Kromdraai caves because of the name of the adjoining farm, was by a group of students from Marist Brothers College in Johannesburg, who explored the caves in 1895 and found fossils embedded in the limestone caverns. However, the man usually credited with finding Sterkfontein is Guglielmo Martinaglia, a lime-worker who blasted the surface openings of the caves in 1896.

Soon thereafter a Mr David Draper from the Geological Society of South Africa explored the caves and reported back to the Society that he had found them most interesting from a geological point of view, and that there was much to be discovered there. Draper was an intrepid explorer and self-taught geologist who pioneered the geological exploration of the Witwatersrand and was respected internationally for his diamond exploration in Brazil. Today, in his honour, the Geological Society of South Africa bestows the Draper medal for outstanding services to geology.

Lime was in great demand by the gold-mining companies for gold processing and by the building industry for the manufacture of cement. It soon became apparent that there was a conflict of interest between geologists and the prospectors and miners who dynamited the lime out of the rocks. Draper's timely intervention in 1897 prevented the caves from being completely destroyed. He successfully persuaded the company that owned the mineral rights to preserve the main cave because of its impressive stalactite and stalagmite formations and its pristine underground lake. Although the main Sterkfontein cavern was thus preserved, blasting operations continued in the immediate vicinity.

At a meeting of the Geological Society of South Africa on 13 September 1897, a Mr ME Frames reported the presence of 'animal remains found in the Kromdraai Caves in the dolomite near Krugersdorp. Amongst these are those of the horse species, antelopes, monkeys, porcupines, rats, bats etc., and the presence of the first two in the cave would lead us to infer that they had been dragged there by beasts of prey' (BROOM & SCHEPERS, 1946:46).

A lime kiln at the Gladysvale site. (IJ)

Surprisingly, although the palaeontological significance of the Sterkfontein area was recognized in the late 19th century, it was not for another three-and-a-half decades that any serious scientific work was undertaken. During this time many specimens were probably destroyed by the lime-mining operations. As the famous fossil finder Robert Broom later wrote, 'It is sad to think that for nearly 40 years no scientist ever paid the slightest attention to these caves; and probably some dozens of skulls of ape-men and all the bones of their skeletons were burnt in lime kilns' (Broom & Schepers, 1946:46).

The caves did, however, attract the attention of tourists, particularly after the discovery of the Taung skull in 1924, when the search for fossils caught the South African public's imagination. Many fossil specimens were found around Sterkfontein by amateur souvenir hunters, and indeed many were offered for sale at the little tearoom next to the main cave. The owner at the time, a Mr RM Cooper (after whom the Coopers site is named), had even written a rough guide to the fossil site in which he used the slogan 'Come to Sterkfontein and buy your guano, and find the missing link', which, as Broom wryly observed, was a 'strangely prophetic remark'.

THE DISCOVERY OF THE TAUNG CHILD

The discovery in 1924 of the Taung child, some 480 kilometres away from the Cradle of Humankind, had a profound effect on the way the world would eventually come to view Africa. The tiny skull, not much bigger than the size of a grapefruit, was blasted out of the lime deposits at Buxton, just outside the village of Taung in the Northern Cape.

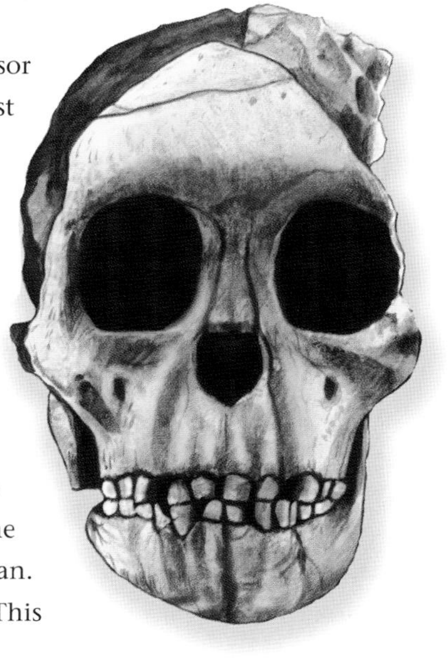

The skull found its way into the hands of Professor Raymond Dart, an Australian who had just taken up the post of Head of Anatomy at Wits University. Dart was immediately struck by the ape-like head and human dentition of the little skull, which suggested it was of a previously unknown species located biologically somewhere between ape and human. Dart worked feverishly once he had the skull in his hands, and the speed with which he made his analysis was a contributing factor to the international controversy that the little skull caused.

Just four months after the discovery, Dart published his findings in the scientific journal *Nature*, announcing that he had found the intermediate creature between ape and man. The international response was overwhelmingly negative. This

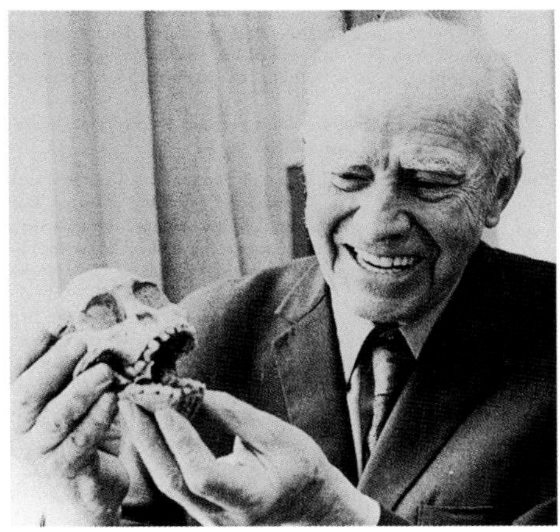

Prof. Dart and the Taung skull. (SAL)

can be attributed to the bias of the time, which held that the origins of humanity lay either in Europe or Asia, to the fact that Dart had been unseemingly hasty in his pronouncements and also because his whole theory was based on a single specimen of a juvenile nature.

It was to take over 20 years before the pendulum of international opinion swung back in Dart's favour, and *Australopithecus africanus* was finally declared to be a part of the human family tree. This recognition was due largely to the efforts of the Scottish-born Dr Robert Broom, an enthusiastic supporter of Dart who came to his defence and found an adult version of the Taung child while working at Sterkfontein. Broom believed that the discovery of another ape-man fossil, particularly an adult specimen, would silence Dart's critics, and at the age of 70, when many others were retiring, this became his mission in life.

From left to right: Dart, Broom, Breuil, and Van Riet Lowe. (MA)

THE ECCENTRIC GENIUS ROBERT BROOM

Broom with one of the many fossils he discovered. (MA)

Robert Broom is one of the most colourful and controversial characters in the history of South African science. The tall, eccentric Scottish-born doctor is best known for his discovery of Mrs Ples, the fossil remains of an adult ape-man, at Sterkfontein in 1947. Broom was 81 years old when he found Mrs Ples. Dart recalled that 'Although [Broom] was a great evolutionist, he was nevertheless a deeply religious man. He even believed spirits led him to his discoveries' (SABC:54).

Broom was born into a poor and very religious family of Plymouth Brethren in Scotland in 1866. He had little formal education and developed his interest in science working as an unpaid lab assistant in the Chemistry Department at the University of Glasgow. He managed to enrol as a medical student and graduated in 1889 with honours in midwifery. He travelled extensively before settling in South Africa in 1898, where he practised medicine to support his true love of palaeontology. He was fortunate to have developed a direct line of communication with the then prime minister, General Jan Smuts. This relationship was to prove very valuable given the number of enemies Broom cultivated during his long career. Smuts had a soft spot for Broom: 'Long years ago I knew him as a medical practitioner in a small South African dorp where medicine kept the family pot boiling while his heart dwelt far away among the reptiles of the Mesozoic age . . .' (Broom & Schepers, 1946:3).

In 1903 Broom was appointed professor of geology and zoology at Victoria College, Stellenbosch, and during the next seven years, with a free railway pass obtained through the South African Museum, he visited every known fossil site in South Africa, and discovered many new ones. Broom spent all his free time exploring the Karoo and from the fossils he found there, he developed a basic framework demonstrating the evolution of mammals from reptiles.

In 1910 the Railways rescinded his free pass when the then minister of railways, JN Sauer, proclaimed that the study and collection of fossils was a matter of no interest to the country. It was partly the attitude of the authorities that impelled him, during a lecture tour to New York in 1913, to sell a number of fossils he had borrowed from the South African Museum in Cape Town to the American Museum of Natural History, prompting outrage among his scientific colleagues.

Broom subsequently furthered his medical studies in Great Britain before resettling in South Africa in 1916. This was the bleakest part of his life, as he felt like an outcast from the scientific community. He practised medicine in the small town of Douglas on the fringes of the Karoo, serving as the mayor of the town in 1920. During that year he was admitted as a Fellow to the Royal Society of South Africa, which restored his spirits somewhat.

Broom had begun to shift his interest to early hominids after hearing of the discovery of Boskop Man, the first human fossil skull found in South Africa. He wrote a paper on it in 1918, labelling it *Homo capensis*.

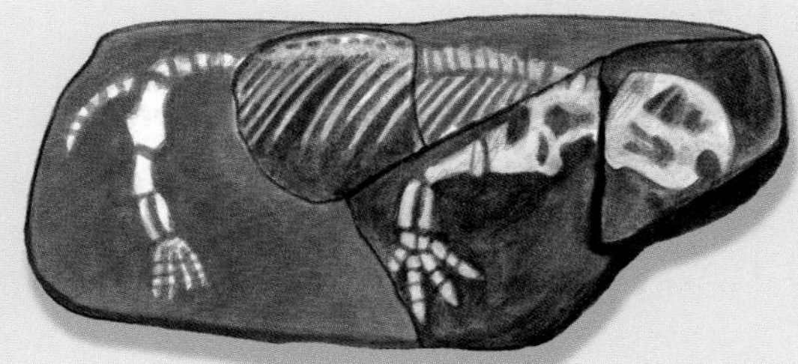

Diictodon feliceps ***fossil discovered by Broom.***

His interest in anthropology was overshadowed by his palaeontological interests. When the Broken Hill skull (now known as Kabwe) was found in 1921 by T Zwigelaar in what is today Zambia, Broom became certain that the origins of humanity must have lain in Africa. Thus, when Taung was discovered, he was very excited. Dart recalls how Broom arrived in his office at Wits in his characteristic black suit and announced: '"I'm Broom. I know your old chiefs . . . I've come to see your little skull." So he came over to the table on which the cardboard box holding the little skull then rested and, dropping on his knees, held it in his hands "in adoration", as he remarked, of "our ancestor"' (SABC:58).

Broom's charisma enabled him to bounce back from the setback of being ostracized by the scientific community and the enormous energy he put into his work earned him the respect of the then prime minister, Jan Smuts, who ensured that a palaeontology post was created for him at the Transvaal Museum in Pretoria in 1934.

During the late thirties and forties Broom concentrated his search for hominins in the Sterkfontein Valley. His work was controversial because of his liberal use of dynamite to extract fossils. However, this approach did produce results that made him world famous by bringing to light Mrs Ples and the Kromdraai Ape-man.

Broom died in 1951, driven fanatically to the end to complete his monograph on the Swartkrans hominins. He completed the final corrections on 6 April 1951 and wrote in his journal 'Now that's finished . . . and so am I'. He passed away that evening.

THE SEARCH MOVES TO STERKFONTEIN

The Taung discovery showed that fossils were most likely to be found where there were extensive lime deposits and it was for this reason that Broom, soon after he had engineered an appointment to a post at the Transvaal Museum in Pretoria in 1934, started concentrating his search on the area of Sterkfontein on the West Rand.

He visited several sites in the area. His hopes were raised and subsequently dashed when a museum colleague informed him that he had come across an ancient-looking human jaw embedded in the cave wall at a cave called Gladysvale, north of Sterkfontein. When Broom investigated he found no trace of the jaw, concluding that it must have been prised loose by souvenir hunters.

However, his luck would change. In July 1936 two of Dart's students, GWH Schepers and H le Riche, visited Sterkfontein and noted the excellent fossil-finding conditions and extensive lime-quarrying taking place there. Bringing out a baboon fossil, they alerted first Dart and then Broom to the site's potential.

Broom made his first trip to Sterkfontein on 9 August 1936. To his delight he discovered that the chief quarryman at Sterkfontein and caretaker of the caves, GW Barlow, had worked at Taung and had been present when the Taung skull was found. He told Broom that he was certain similar skulls had been found at Sterkfontein and promised to keep a sharp lookout for such specimens in the future.

Broom was lucky. Three days later, on 12 August, he visited Sterkfontein again and Barlow gave him 'three nice little fossil baboon skulls and much of the skull of a large sabre-toothed tiger' (Broom & Schepers, 1946:46). His interest was piqued, and he began searching the area with more vigour. On 17 August, only his third visit to Sterkfontein, Broom was handed the blasted-out natural brain cast of an anthropoid by Barlow, who asked 'Is this what you're after?' Broom replied 'That's what I'm after' (Broom & Schepers, 1946:46). These words marked the beginning of a new chapter in the study of human origins.

Barlow showed Broom where he'd found the skull and the Scottish doctor soon unearthed a rather battered and incomplete skull, jawbone and teeth of what appeared to be an adult australopithecine. However, as Broom studied his find he came to believe that the teeth and other elements of his specimen differed markedly from those of the Taung child, so much so that in his view it was a different species altogether. This was a characteristic peculiarity for which Broom would become famous: the naming of a new species or genus with almost every fossil discovery.

Eventually he settled on a name for his new find, *Plesianthropus transvaalensis* (Near Man from the Transvaal), assigning the fossils not only to a new species, but to a new genus as well. The search for human origins was beginning to get complicated.

Broom's excitement at his new find was dampened by the reaction of the international

A BLAST FROM THE PAST

The fossil extraction techniques of the early 20th century were brutal to say the least. Dynamite was an essential part of the fossil finder's tool kit well into the late 1940s.

The preferred method of breaking up the concrete-like breccia that housed most of the Cradle fossils was literally to blast them out. While these techniques certainly succeeded in bringing fossils to the surface, they also did incalculable harm by obliterating the context in which the fossils were formed, and undoubtedly destroying many of the fossils themselves.

The trend was set at Taung, where fossils were routinely blasted out of the lime quarry at the northern Cape village by workers trying to separate lime from the calcified stone. This procedure was repeated at Sterkfontein and other fossil sites in the Cradle area during the 1930s, and most of the fossils brought to the attention of Robert Broom were the products of mining activities.

It was only in the 1940s that reason prevailed among palaeontologists, who began to realize the dangers of indiscriminate dynamiting. Broom in particular came in for heavy criticism of his blasting techniques and was at one time legally prevented from blasting by representatives of the National Monuments Council. However, he solicited the support of the then prime minister, Jan Smuts, and received clearance to carry on. Undeterred by criticism and dressed in his trademark black suit, he could be seen crawling around on his hands and knees as the dust cleared, 'sifting earth, peering into obscure corners and inspecting tiny fragments' (Terry, 1974).

An early Sterkfontein excavation. (MA)

scientific community, which, as a result of discoveries in China in 1931, still favoured Asia as the birthplace of humankind and was not very interested in finds of 'apes' from Africa. His determination remaining intact despite international scepticism, Broom redoubled his efforts and continued his search in the foothills around Sterkfontein.

THE FIRST 'ROBUST' APE-MAN

On 8 June 1938, the quarryman Barlow contacted Broom and said that he had found something special: it appeared to be part of an australopithecine palate and a first molar. Broom was puzzled because the matrix in which the fossil was set was different from the rock around Sterkfontein. It was also far more robust than the type of specimen he was looking for. After being questioned, Barlow revealed that the fossil had not been found at Sterkfontein, but by a schoolboy, Gert Terreblanche, on the neighbouring farm of Kromdraai, some 1,5 kilometres away.

Broom immediately set out for the farm, only to find that Gert was at school. He persuaded the boy's sister to take him to the hillside where the fossils had been found. After fossicking in the dust, Broom found a fossil tooth. This find was enough to persuade him to hurry straight to the young Terreblanche's school.

At the school Broom explained his mission to the principal and Gert was duly summoned to his office. The boy produced four fossil teeth from his pocket, which Broom persuaded him to surrender for a shilling apiece. Under the Scottish doctor's gentle interrogation he admitted to having prised the teeth out of what appeared to be a jawbone embedded in the rocks.

Broom wanted to return to the site immediately, but the principal pointed out that there was still another hour-and-a-half of school time, and suggested that Broom lecture the children on the importance of fossils and how caves were formed.

Broom, dressed as always in the formal black suit and starched wing collar that gave him the appearance of grave authority, had no difficulty enthralling his young audience with his tales of searching for fossils. Once the class was over, Gert took Broom to the fossil site, where Broom found the skull from which the teeth had been taken. Although the skull had been smashed by the schoolboy's crude dental extraction, there were sufficient fragments to allow for reconstruction. This material, plus a further tooth that Gert had stashed away, was handed over in exchange for five chocolate bars.

The whole area was subsequently searched thoroughly and the topsoil carefully sieved by members of the Transvaal Museum staff. The result was the discovery of major portions of the skull that could be adequately reconstructed – but it varied considerably from earlier finds. It was altogether more massive, particularly the jaw, which supported unusually large molars. Broom, after recovering and cleaning the specimen, pronounced the find a new species of ape-man, *Paranthropus robustus* (a robust creature akin to man).

The discovery of the Kromdraai Fossil (labelled TM 1517) marked a turning point in world opinion, as the significance of the fossils coming out of South Africa could no longer be ignored. After visiting Sterkfontein and studying the australopithecine specimens Broom had recovered, two leading American scientists, William K Gregory and Milo Hellman, concluded that these were 'in both a structural and a genetic sense the conservative cousins of the contemporary human branch' (Gregory, 1939).

Buoyed by this support, Broom began further excavations at Kromdraai in 1941, but his mood gradually turned to disappointment as the sterile breccia revealed few fossils of significance, with the exception of a juvenile australopithecine jaw. Broom closed down the site and, during the years of the Second World War, focused on writing an overview of the significance of the ape-men. He published his findings in 1946, shortly before he turned 80. His conclusions confirmed Dart's original hypothesis that the australopithecines had walked upright and that, although they had small brains and ape-like faces, their teeth were human-like. Broom's analysis led him to believe that they had the ability to use tools and that, based on the animals he found with them, they probably lived in open country.

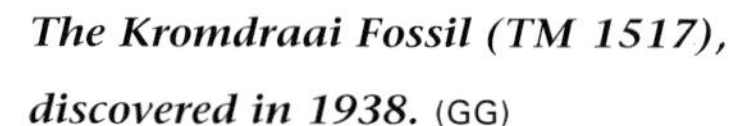

The Kromdraai Fossil (TM 1517), discovered in 1938. (GG)

In 1947 Broom and his new assistant, JT Robinson, renewed the excavations at Sterkfontein, using dynamite to blast away the hard breccia in which they hoped to find hominin fossils. Their heavy-handed techniques raised the ire of other scientists, who argued, with some justification, that explosives destroyed the context of the fossils, making it impossible to date them. Broom's response was that the rock-hard nature of the sediments left him little choice but to employ such drastic measures, and that the caves held little context in any case.

The National Monuments Council disagreed and banned Broom from further work at Sterkfontein unless he was accompanied by a field geologist. Broom, who had served as a professor of geology and zoology at Victoria College in Stellenbosch, was outraged and appealed to Prime Minister Smuts, among others, for support. The Commission backed down and a defiant Broom continued blasting at Sterkfontein. Within a few days his efforts paid off.

Broom and Robinson at Sterkfontein. (MA)

MRS PLES

On 18 April 1947, Broom and Robinson blasted an almost complete australopithecine skull out of the Sterkfontein Cave wall. The blast had split the skull into two fragments, but had not damaged the specimen irreparably. The skull was clearly that of an adult version of the Taung child, and Broom believed it to have been that of a middle-aged female. Broom christened the find *Plesianthropus africanus*, which the media soon shortened to 'Mrs Ples'. Broom was later to write: 'I have seen many interesting sights in my long life but this was the most thrilling in my experience' (Terry, 1974).

The remarkable string of finds would continue. On 1 August that same year, Broom and Robinson blasted out a slab of breccia that contained the partial thigh bone, several vertebrae and more or less intact pelvis of an australopithecine. These remains, labelled Sts 14, proved that australopithecines were indeed upright walkers, or bipeds. Although the pelvic bones were smaller than those of modern humans they were not wholly dissimilar in shape and form, whereas they were very markedly different from those of apes. By the end of 1947, Broom had amassed further specimens, including a lower jaw with teeth.

Mrs Ples, or Sts 5 (her museum catalogue number), represented a vital turning point in the broader acceptance of South African australopithecines as hominins. The discovery of an adult cranium negated criticism that the Taung child was nothing more than a juvenile ape. Sts 5 demonstrated without doubt that had the Taung child grown up, it would not have developed into a chimpanzee or gorilla.

The discovery of Mrs Ples captured the imagination of the international scientific community and South African fossil hunters began receiving more support. In 1947 the British Association offered Broom 'its congratulations on the brilliant success of his recent exploration of the Sterkfontein site. His new discoveries amplify and confirm in a remarkable way his interpretation of the earlier finds and also provide a vindication of the general view put forward by Professor Raymond Dart in his report of the first *Australopithecus* skull found in 1924' (Berger & Hilton-Barber, 2000).

'Since one of the two ape-men seemed clearly to be on the line of human descent and the other to have specialised away from that line, Broom's finds compelled scholars to realise that not all early hominids were direct ancestors of modern mankind. Some were on side branches. This meant that at an earlier period the two species, so closely related to each other, must have branched off from a common ancestor. The pattern of hominid evolution was not like a linear Chain of Being after all. It was like a bush of branches, only one of which made the grade to the later stages of human evolution, while the other branches were doomed to ultimate extinction' (PHILLIP TOBIAS, 1994).

In 1948 Broom switched his attention to the nearby site of Swartkrans, just across the valley from Sterkfontein, where he and Robinson found several more hominins. In 1950 Broom and Robinson produced a preliminary description of Sts 14, but it was not until 1972 that Robinson, who became renowned for his authoritative studies of australopithecine teeth, published a detailed description of the find. Robinson continued working on the block of breccia from which the Sts 14 pelvis came, recovering a number of previously unknown vertebrae and ribs, adding greatly to our understanding of the locomotion of those particular hominins.

THE IMPORTANCE OF MRS PLES

Why is Mrs Ples one of the most important characters in South Africa's fossil family? The 2,5-million-year-old ape-man fossil provided the evidence that Raymond Dart needed to prove that the Taung child was an intermediate genus between human and ape, and that humanity's roots were in fact African.

Mrs Ples, coined from the scientific appellation *Plesianthropus transvaalensis*, was later reclassified as *Australopithecus africanus* once the skull had been studied in greater detail by other scientists.

In early 2002, after renewed studies of Mrs Ples, palaeoanthropologist Francis Thackeray concluded that the skull was that of a male. However, it is unlikely that Mrs Ples will be renamed Mr Ples.

Mrs Ples. (GG)

After the highlights of the forties, the fifties were in many ways a depressing time for palaeoanthropology. Few exciting fossils were found and funding was consequently harder to come by. The rise to power of the National Party in 1948, with its fundamentalist and separatist views, effectively ended any chance of government support scientists might have enjoyed. The ousted prime minister, Jan Smuts, had displayed a keen personal interest in human evolution, to the point of encouraging his son to study the geology of Stone Age sites. This passion was unfortunately not shared by his successors. Indeed, the new prime minister, DF Malan, was philosophically wary of the unbiblical notion that humankind had evolved from an ape-like ancestor, and the notion of common ancestry did not suit the emergent apartheid ideology.

Despite the negative attitude of the government of the time and the lack of funding, the fifties witnessed a breakthrough in the understanding of the complicated cave systems in the dolomites. The relationship between fossils and the caves in which they were found had always troubled scientists because of the lack of a generally accepted cohesive interpretive framework. This problem was solved by the efforts of a young geologist who had been invited by Robinson to conduct a detailed study of the geology of the Swartkrans site shortly before it was closed down in 1951.

Charles Kimberlin ('Bob') Brain's work at Swartkrans and other caves was eventually published as his PhD in 1958, titled *The Ape-Man Bearing Cave Deposits of the Transvaal*. During this time, working with Revil Mason and Alun Hughes, Brain found the first evidence that early hominins in the Cradle had been stone tool makers.

The other seminal work to come out of the 1950s was Revil Mason's *Prehistory of the Transvaal*, published in 1962, in which Mason introduced a mathematical approach to working out the complicated relationships between South African Stone Age cultures.

THE ART OF STUDYING THE GRAVE

Brain succeeded Broom and Robinson when he was appointed palaeontologist at the Transvaal Museum in 1965, and one of his first actions was to revive the Swartkrans dig, which had been dormant for 12 years. Brain's thorough analysis of the Swartkrans fossils led him to the conclusion that most of the bones were accumulated in the caves by scavengers and predators that used the caves as feeding and breeding lairs.

This raised an interesting philosophical question that challenged the theory argued by Dart in the late forties, namely that the fossil bones were the result of bloodthirsty fighting between killer apes who bludgeoned each other to death with weapons made of bone. This idea, formally labelled the osteodontokeratic culture (bone, tooth and horn), gained such popularity that Stanley Kubrik used it in his opening sequence of the film *2001: A Space Odyssey*.

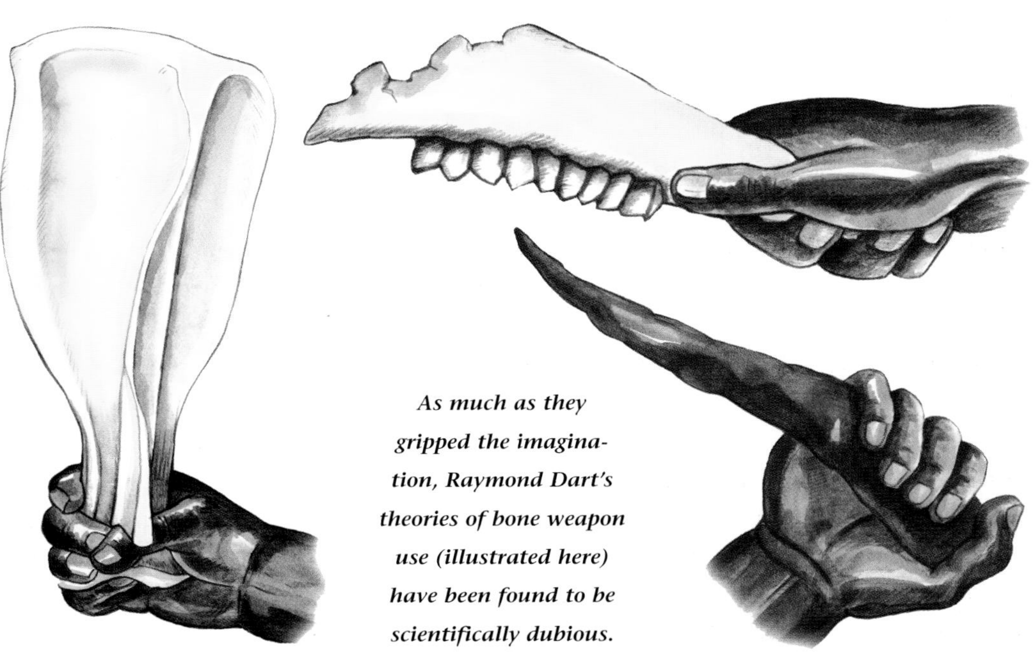

As much as they gripped the imagination, Raymond Dart's theories of bone weapon use (illustrated here) have been found to be scientifically dubious.

Through a series of compelling and elegantly simple comparative studies of modern accumulating agents such as hyenas, leopards and porcupines, Brain proved conclusively that the fossils in the cave sites were not collected by early hominins, but by animals. Our ancient heritage was not bathed in the blood of violence between our ancestors – we were the hunted, not the hunters. In making such a convincing case, Brain almost single-handedly founded a new field of science, now known as the science of taphonomy, or study of the grave.

Brain's 1965 re-opening of Swartkrans began a 25-year excavation that would not only make Swartkrans the second-richest site for hominin fossils (Sterkfontein being the first) but also set the standard by which all future excavations of South African caves would be judged.

At the same time that Brain was embarking on his revolutionary studies, another significant development occurred. Sterkfontein was saved from obscurity and possible destruction in the early sixties when the land on which the caves stand was donated by the Stegman family to the University of the Witwatersrand. Phillip Tobias was a prime motivator in rescuing the site and renewing the excavations, which began again in 1966, the same year that the little Robert Broom Museum was opened at the caves.

For years there was almost no reward for the hard work of removing tons of breccia from Sterkfontein, a labour-intensive exercise that occurred under the supervision of a heavy-set Welshman, Alun Hughes. Ten years of hard work yielded only 50 or so assorted hominin fragments, which were difficult to interpret because most weren't found *in situ*.

Hughes spent two or three days a week at the site supervising the ten excavators and preparators employed by the University, patiently cataloguing the few finds that emerged from the rubble. A grid system was established, consisting of steel girders, wire and nylon fishing line. The excavation was conducted in spits that measured one yard by one foot.

It was not until 1976 that the first significant hominin was recovered from a context that could be clearly identified. Stw 53 was the first evidence of a new type of hominin at Sterkfontein, one that was more advanced than the australopithecines, and thus difficult to place in a taxonomic category. Initially classified as *Homo habilis* because of its less protruding face, head shape, tooth-wear pattern and larger brain capacity, it was later argued that it might be *H. ergaster* or even an advanced australopithecine; the jury is still out.

Alun Hughes. (PF)

In 1978 geologist Tim Partridge came up with a geological model for interpreting Sterkfontein's complicated stratigraphy. He introduced the concept of 'members' for the deposits, labelling them in sequence from oldest to youngest, Member 1 being the oldest deposit, dating back possibly beyond the

THE HUNTERS OR THE HUNTED?

We cannot but view our history through the prejudices of our present. Raymond Dart served as a medical orderly in the First World War and the slaughter that the Allies and the Germans visited on each other had a profound effect on his world-view. For Dart the horror of war seemed to indicate that humanity was inherently aggressive, and so, when he came across the smashed bones of australopithecines at Makapansgat, he was predisposed to believe that the australopithecines were killer apes and that the violence they had inflicted on one another was in some way genetically imprinted into all subsequent hominin species, including our own.

Bob Brain refuted Dart's killer ape theories by proving that most hominin fossils found in caves are there as a result of the actions of animals. His conclusion was that our most ancient ape-like ancestors were more likely to have been victims of carnivores as opposed to victims of each other's aggression. Brain continued his experiments and detailed observations on cave accumulations and the accumulating habits of predators and scavengers in a lateral way. He studied the remains of San hunter-gatherer meals in the Kalahari and even fed antelope skeletons to captured cheetah and leopard to find out which parts of the skeleton were most likely to escape consumption. With this work Brain almost single-handedly founded the fledgling science of taphonomy – the study of the grave – as applied to our hominin ancestors. Today his work continues to be built upon by young researchers.

Bob Brain undertook a detailed study of leopard behaviour to understand how fossils ended up in caves. (GG)

Studies of bone assemblages derived from the activities of leopard, hyena, porcupine and eagle are under way throughout the Cradle of Humankind. Experiments in tool making and bone weathering are being undertaken. Much of Brain's work has been shown to be fundamental to the ongoing scientific process. New findings continue to confirm that we are not descended from killer apes, as Dart thought, but from what should be considered just another African animal, one that was in fact more the hunted than the hunter.

PHILLIP TOBIAS

Phillip Tobias is one of the luminaries of South African science and a world authority on human evolution. Born in Durban on 14 October 1925, Tobias has had a great influence on palaeoanthropology in the second half of the 20th century. He has received no less than 21 international prizes, medals and awards for his contribution to the science, holds 11 honorary degrees and has authored almost 800 scientific articles over the course of his career.

Phillip Tobias has played an enormous role in popularizing palaeoanthropology. (GG)

He graduated from Wits Medical School in 1946 with a BSc, and received his PhD in 1951. He was one of Raymond Dart's students and eventually succeeded him as the head of anatomy and ultimately the dean of the Medical School at Wits.

In the early sixties he was invited by Louis and Mary Leakey to describe the first robust australopithecine found in East Africa. *Zinjanthropus boisei* was nicknamed 'The Nutcracker Man', after Tobias, in awe of its massive dental structure, commented that its teeth resembled a set of nutcrackers. He was also involved in the description of the first *Homo habilis* fossils found in East Africa.

Tobias was instrumental in reviving Sterkfontein during the mid-sixties and, along with supervisor Alun Hughes, amassed the remains of over 500 individual hominin specimens from the site.

During the apartheid years he was one of the few South African scientists who was entertained by international institutions during the academic boycott.

Tobias retired as the head of the Wits anatomy department in 1990 but continued directing palaeoanthropology research until 1997 when he was succeeded by Lee Berger. In 1999 he accepted an honorary position as director of the Sterkfontein Research Unit and assisted Ron Clarke with the description of Little Foot.

3-million-year mark, while Member 6 is the youngest at a mere 100 000 to 200 000 years old. The richest deposit for hominin material so far has been Member 4, which contained most of the *africanus* specimens recovered from Sterkfontein to date.

By the late 1980s excavations at Sterkfontein were penetrating down into a partially decalcified cavity that has often been referred to as the 'swallow hole', owing to its abundance of australopithecine fossils. Almost all of the specimens from this cavity, which measures approximately 8 x 10 metres, are relatively well preserved, with very little crushing. The 'swallow hole' is the deep excavated area in the centre of the site (see diagram below).

By 1989, Hughes and Tobias had catalogued some 550 hominin specimens from Sterkfontein alone. The two men had been collecting fossils almost continually since 1966.

Across the valley at Swartkrans, Brain was also making headway. In a quarter of a century of his custodianship of the site, 350 000 fossil pieces had been recovered. Brain's approach to site excavation set the standards for subsequent digs. It is a little known fact that almost every site in the Cradle of Humankind today is dug based on methods devised and implemented by Bob Brain at Swartkrans.

In the course of this work, Brain would also make dramatic discoveries about our origins. He would find evidence of, and subsequently prove, the earliest controlled use of fire on the planet, more than 1 million years ago. Brain insists that the story told by Swartkrans was that 'far from being mighty hunters, the early hominids formed an insignificant part of the fauna of the time and they were certainly subservient to carnivores such as leopards and sabre-tooth cats. They had been the hunted, rather than the hunters' (Brain [i], 1981).

Brain also demonstrated the existence of a bone tool culture, possibly used by the robust australopithecines. The wear patterns on sharpened bones he found at Swartkrans and other sites led him to believe that stones were not the only form of early tool, and that the use of tools by early hominins was more widespread than had previously been imagined. By 1990 the Cradle of Humankind projects undertaken by the Transvaal Museum and Wits University were at a crossroads. Tobias was approaching retirement, Brain was completing his Swartkrans study – and funds were drying up.

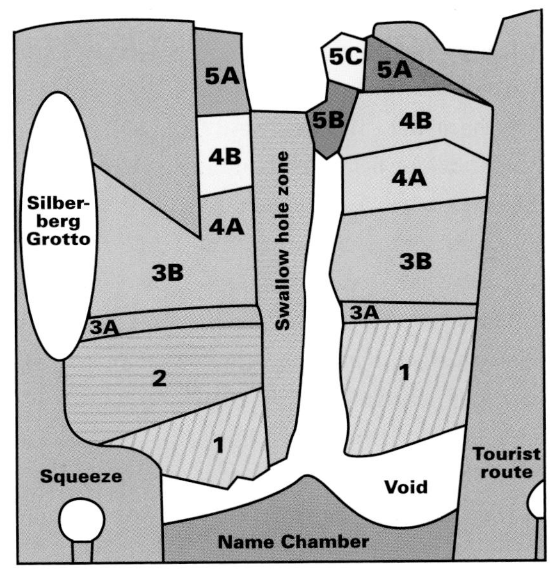

Sterkfontein Members (1 is oldest, 5 is most recent).

André Keyser with an australopithecine skull found at Drimolen. (GG)

GLADYSVALE AND DRIMOLEN: A NEW ERA

Then came Gladysvale. The site that had originally been explored by Broom, and then Tobias, yielded the first new hominin material in 1991, making Gladysvale the first new hominin site discovered in South Africa in 44 years. A Wits University team led by Lee Berger found an australopithecine tooth, the first of a dozen hominin remains and thousands of other fossils that would be unearthed. In terms of quantity of fossil-bearing breccia, Gladysvale is the largest fossil deposit in the Cradle of Humankind.

Shortly afterwards, geologist André Keyser found the remains of robust australopithecines at the nearby site of Drimolen. These two discoveries generated a new surge of interest in palaeoanthropology, and highlighted the importance of South Africa as a locus for the search for human origins.

Berger and Johannesburg art dealer Mark Read, whose family owns the Plover's Lake site in the Cradle of Humankind, discussed the need to raise funds to exploit the new finds and came up with the idea of creating a non-profit organization along the lines of the Leakey Foundation, which had raised considerable sums of money for scientific research in East Africa.

THE EXCAVATORS: UNSUNG HEROES

Over the years most of the actual digging of the Sterkfontein site has been conducted by a dedicated group of men who work five days a week, 48 weeks a year to extract fossils from the hard breccias found at the site. Several of the men have been working at the site since its opening in 1966 and have made an invaluable but often unrecognized contribution to the furthering of our understanding of human origins. But the public's recognition of their efforts is growing. With the discovery in 1997 of Little Foot, the oldest australopithecine yet found in South Africa, the two men who actually found the specimen deep in the underground cave were given recognition for the remarkable achievement. For Stephen Motsumi and Nkwane Molefe, finding the matching tibial fragments was as difficult as finding the proverbial needle in a haystack.

As times have changed in South Africa, so has the level of recognition of the critical role played by the mostly black field technicians, the people at the front line of palaeoanthropological research in the Cradle of Humankind.

Excavators Joseph Sekowe (foreground) and Lucas Mothobi at Coopers. (GG)

THE TAMING OF FIRE

Swartkrans has produced the oldest evidence yet discovered of the domestic use of fire. During his excavations, Bob Brain discovered 20 spits or hearths in a section of the cave, the oldest being over a million years old.

Of the 350 000 or so pieces of bone found at Swartkrans, 270 appear to have been deliberately burnt. In a series of comparative studies, Bob Brain showed that the burnt bone remains were consistent with the results produced when bones were burnt in experimental campfires made from White Stinkwood (*Celtis africana*), one of the most common trees of the area. Controlled fires appear to have occurred repeatedly in the gulley as it was filling up, indicating long-term use by hominins.

Brain has noted that it is 'likely that fire management was based on fire gathered from natural conflagrations caused by lightning strikes, with the ability to make fire at will only coming much later. But even this kind of management was a technological advance of immense significance, giving early hominids a measure of protection from predators, badly needed when sheltering in caves at night' (Brain [ii], 1998).

(RDT)

They attracted the interest of Anglo-American chairman Gavin Relly, who helped launch the Palaeo-Anthropology Scientific Trust (PAST) in 1994 and put together a team of South African businessmen and -women to ensure continued funding for the important work being carried out.

PAST very quickly succeeded in raising funding for a number of headline-grabbing projects. One of these was the 'bird of prey hypothesis' developed by Berger and Ron Clarke, who had taken over the supervision of Sterkfontein after the death of Alun Hughes in 1993.

The Gladysvale australopithecine teeth. (LB)

LITTLE FOOT

The South African palaeoanthropological renaissance started to gain momentum after the first democratic elections in South Africa in 1994. The end of the academic boycott and lifting of international sanctions against South Africa allowed it to re-enter the scientific mainstream. PAST's fund-raising efforts, combined with re-awakened international interest in South Africa, gave the science a boost – and created an ideal environment for the emergence of Little Foot.

The story of Little Foot is characterized by a remarkable chain of coincidences. The little australopithecine skeleton might well never have seen the light of day had it not been for the persistence of Ron Clarke, the field officer at Sterkfontein, appointed after Alun Hughes' death in 1993. In 1994 Clarke was going through some bags of previously collected material when he found a number of hominin foot bones that had been overlooked. These 12 little bones displayed a mixture of ape and human characteristics, showing that their owner had been comfortable both walking on the ground and climbing in trees. The find was named Stw 573. Three years later Clarke was rummaging through other fossils stored in the Wits strongroom when he found a foot bone (intermediate cuneiform) which fitted that of Stw 573. Clarke found several other bones that pieced together the foot and ankle bones of Stw 573 and showed that it was more ape-like than human. The bags from which the bones were found convinced him that the rest of the skeleton must still be in the Sterkfontein caves, most likely in an area known as the Silberberg Grotto.

At the end of June 1997 he gave a cast of the distal fragment of the right tibia to two of the fossil preparators at Sterkfontein, Stephen Motsumi and Nkwane Molefe, and asked them to search the cave surface of the Grotto. 'The task I had set them was like looking for a needle in a haystack, as the grotto is an enormous, deep, dark cavern with breccia exposed on the walls, floor and ceiling. After two days of searching with the aid of hand-held lamps, they found it on 3 July 1997 near the bottom of the Member 2 talus slope at the western end of the grotto. The fit was perfect, despite the bone having been blasted apart by lime-workers 65 or more years previously' (Clarke, 1998).

For the next year the three men chiselled away at the hard rock, trying to expose the rest of the skeleton. To their consternation, they found that an ancient collapse of the cave wall had separated the top part of the skeleton from the lower part. In September 1998 they found part of the arm bones and a portion of the skull. The skeleton is still embedded in the rock, so a detailed analysis of what it might be still has to be carried out. Clarke says initial indications are that it is an australopithecine, but that it seems to have unusual characteristics compared to the other specimens of that genus found at Sterkfontein. Initially Partridge, Clarke and others dated Little Foot at 3,3 million years old. However, a revised dating model published in 2002 by Berger and others suggests that it may be a million years younger. Nonetheless Little Foot is the most complete australopithecine early hominin yet discovered in South Africa.

BIRD OF PREY HYPOTHESIS

In 1993, during an excavation at the Gladysvale Cave, Lee Berger witnessed an extraordinary sight. A pair of Black Eagles homed in on a colony of vervet monkeys close by the dig, and while one eagle acted as a decoy, the other swooped down and grabbed a monkey before flying away with the limp primate in its talons.

The event was remarkable in its synchronicity, as Berger had been thinking about one of the enduring mysteries of the Taung skull. Since its discovery by Dart in 1924, a plausible explanation had yet to be found for a depressed fragment on the top of the little australopithecine's brain case. Working on a hunch that the damage may have been caused by an ancient African eagle, Berger tracked down the Black Eagle nest. At the bottom of the cliff where the nest was located he found in the undergrowth the skull of a juvenile baboon that had almost exactly the same depressed piece of bone that could be seen on the back of the tiny Taung skull.

Working with Ron Clarke, Berger studied the fossil bones associated with Taung and other sites and found that the Taung fossil types were consistent with the remains found around the nests of African eagles. Their paper, published in 1995, provided strong circumstantial evidence that the Taung child had been the victim of an ancient African eagle. This seemed to confirm Brain's theory that the australopithecines were more victims of their environment than the aggressive killer apes described by Raymond Dart.

A modern-day Black Eagle. (SIL)

Nkwane Molefe, Ron Clarke and Stephen Motsumi with the Little Foot tibia. (TS/BD)

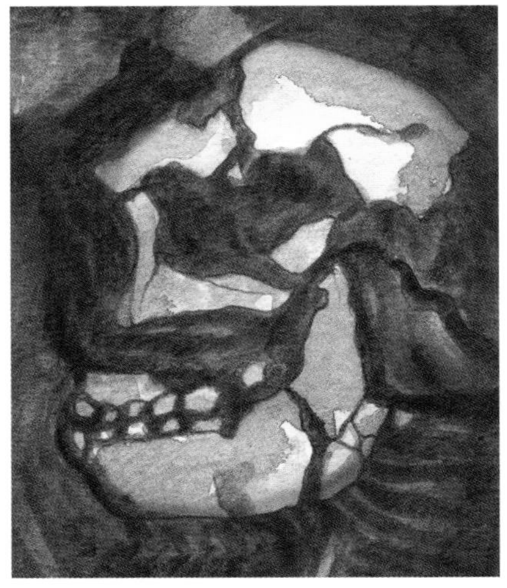

Part of the buried skull belonging to Little Foot.

'Alun Hughes used to tell me of a recurrent dream that he had of his breaking into a cavern and finding a complete skeleton of an Australopithecus *lying there. I am pleased, through strange circumstances, it has been my good fortune to realize Alun's dream and bring to fruition the expectations of Phillip Tobias that an archaic form of* Australopithecus *would be recovered from the lowest levels of Sterkfontein.'*

RON CLARKE

By 1998 the South African palaeoanthropological revival was in full swing. A major international scientific convention, the Dual Congress, was held that year. It showcased the South African view of human origins and demonstrated that a unique evolutionary pattern was unfolding south of the Limpopo, one that was different from the East African model.

PAST has become the largest palaeoanthropological fundraising body in the world, sponsoring some 14 excavations in southern Africa, many of these located within the Cradle of Humankind.

COOPERS

What Little Foot had demonstrated was that established fossil sites still had as much potential for surprise as new sites. This was also to prove the case with Coopers, a site situated midway between Kromdraai and Sterkfontein. Coopers had looked promising way back in the 1930s, when a researcher named Middleton-Shaw had found a single hominin tooth there. At the time there was some controversy surrounding the find, fuelled by accusations that the tooth had actually been taken from Sterkfontein by one of the students. Brain examined Coopers during the 1950s and came to the conclusion that it could not conclusively be considered a hominin site.

While the original Coopers tooth went missing during the 1960s or 70s from the Wits dental school where it was housed, another tooth from Coopers cropped up at the Transvaal Museum in 1994. There, Martin Pickford came across a single tooth in a collection of boxes marked 'Coopers'. In a paper written by Lee Berger, Pickford and Francis Thackeray, it was suggested that the tooth appeared to belong to *Homo*, but because it was found out of context this could not be stated beyond doubt.

Berger decided to revisit Coopers and began a test excavation at a part of the site known as Coopers A. He sent one of his students, Christine Steininger, to the Transvaal Museum to study the fossilized fauna from Brain's excavation. To her surprise she found a badly crushed hominin face in the boxes. Berger halted the excavations while he and Steininger studied the skull and concluded that it was that of a robust ape-man. In May 2001 Berger resumed his work at Coopers A and within three weeks his team found another two robust molars, the first Coopers fossils to be recovered *in situ*.

Under their scrutiny Coopers began to yield more and more finds. Pieces of fossilized hominin, extinct animals and stone tools emerged. Coopers has now joined the ranks of the richest fossil-bearing sites in the Cradle of Humankind, and may well be the basis of another five decades of scientific investigation.

The history of Coopers demonstrates that there is probably still much to be discovered, not only at Coopers itself, but also at other sites in the Cradle of Humankind.

THE CHANGING FACE OF EXCAVATION

Students, scientists and visitors assist in digging fossils from the ground at sites around the Cradle of Humankind, but day in and day out, the people who do most of the work are the permanent field technicians.

The traditional role of a field technician as someone who merely carried breccia or wielded a pick has changed dramatically. Now, the field technicians are educated individuals, many pursuing higher degrees, who perform all the functions of a scientific assistant on site. From laser mapping using a theodolite, to fossil identification in the field and laboratory, the modern field technician is a trained, skilled, and critical part of the research team.

The number of women on site has also increased dramatically over the past few years, and most of the newer sites now boast at least 50 per cent gender equity.

Irene Maphofa (foreground) and Johannes Msetywa excavating the Coopers site. (GG)

Paranthropus robustus *defending its territory.* (NG)

PART TWO
WINDOWS *on the past*

The problem with history is that time turns to dust the bodies and blood of those who made it. Trying to understand what life was like for our earliest ancestors is particularly difficult as the drama of their everyday lives took place beyond the boundaries of memory. Indeed, for most of us, it is hard to imagine a life without the modern comforts that we have become so dependent on. Yet for all the advantages of 21st-century social structures and lifestyles, we have in many ways become alienated from the environment we evolved from. Almost all of us are now observers of the natural world rather than participants in it. Our ancestors, whose lives were deeply integrated with the landscape they lived in, would have had a radically different perception of how the world worked.

This part of the guide is a combination of speculation and science. The first chapter of Part Two comprises an imaginary description – based on scientific evidence – of hominin life as it might have been at different periods of our most ancient past.

The next chapter is an updated guide to all the hominin species that are known to have existed. The exact relationships between these species and the debates as to which ones were central to the evolution of modern humans remain controversial, and may never be resolved in a universally satisfactory way.

The third chapter in this part is a guide to the fossil sites of the Cradle of Humankind, those wonderful outdoor laboratories in which the science of reading the past is practised. It is no understatement to say that these fossil sites have significantly shaped the way palaeoanthropologists view humanity's ancient past. This chapter details the significant discoveries at each of the major fossil sites and provides a brief history and description of the sites themselves.

CHAPTER *four*

SNAPSHOTS IN TIME

The landscape and ecology of the Cradle of Humankind have not always been as they are today. The more open savannas and clinging gallery woodlands around the small streams are a relatively recent phenomenon. In fact, the whole area has changed dramatically over time, with wet and dry periods driven by tropical interludes followed by eons of cooler, more temperate climatic conditions.

Artist Walter Voigt has created the paintings on the following pages to provide us with a window on days gone by. The images are all taken from a single vantage point near Kromdraai overlooking many of the major sites in the area, including Sterkfontein, Swartkrans, Coopers and Bolt's Farm. These images give an impression of what it would be like to stand in one spot and watch the changes in the land, plants and animals of the region, as well as in the culture and behaviour of hominins, over the last 3 million years.

All the animals and plants in the images are based on actual finds in the area and represent, to the best of our ability at this time, the way scientists view the past.

2,5 MILLION YEARS AGO

The yellow-brown grass slopes roll gently down to the edge of the dense tropical woodland where giant trees snaked with liana vines reach into the thick, humid air. The sound of water from the green river beyond the riverine gallery mingles with the grunts of the ancestral hippo, *Hippopotamus gorgops*, and is carried up the hill on the back of a warm breeze. The calls of birds and numerous monkeys, such as the colobus-like cercopithecoides, pierce the air but cause no alarm to the small near-horse, about the size of a Shetland pony, that steps gingerly from the tree line with an unusual gait. *Hipparion*, the three-toed extinct cousin of the living one-toed horse, thrived for millions of years in this broken woodland, sharing its environment with *Sivatheres*, the huge, short-necked ancestral giraffe with antlers like those of a moose, and a variety of antelope, both browsers and grazers.

High above the circling Martial Eagles, dark, heavy summer rain clouds patiently build up to what will be a violent late afternoon storm. Where the bush is less thick the fleeting shapes of the extinct elephant, *Elephas recki*, can be seen eating patches of grass. They cohabit peacefully with the extinct, distant relative of the musk ox, *Makapania*. As the slopes rise away from the river, the bush thins out until it becomes open grassland, studded with acacia-like trees, in between which graze herds of antelope. This is also the terrain of *Chasmaporthetes*, the extinct hunting hyena that inhabited the caves of Swartkrans and Sterkfontein, and of the small extinct baboon *Parapapio*.

A tremendous roar slices through the heat, and in an instant the *Hipparion* and *Sivatheres* vanish into the refuge of the thick bush. The antelope kick their heels and disappear over the horizon line, while the monkeys hoot and howl from the top of the forest canopy. The sabre-tooth cat that roared is not visible. Is it the great *Homotherium*, the larger-than-lion-sized predator, or could it be the terrifying leopard-sized *Dinofelis*, the so-called false sabre-tooth, both of which may have stalked the dense bush for prey? After a long silence in which the creatures of the broken woodland and riverine bush assess the danger, the chorus of bushveld voices gradually returns. They are interrupted again by a growling scuffle as *Megantereon*, the 'dirk-toothed' cat, tries to steal the cached kill of a leopard from the lower branches of an ancient acacia-like tree, but in the face of stiff resistance from the leopard, abandons its efforts and lopes away.

From the safety of the upper branches of a nearby tall, grey-barked *Ficus*, an ape-like creature slowly descends, carefully reaching for each new handhold and testing its weight before committing to the next limb. *Australopithecus africanus* displays an unnerving mixture of human and animal characteristics. There is a human-like consciousness evident behind its sharp brown eyes, but the rest of its face is distinctly ape-like. That is until it grins, parting the protruding black lips that conceal large teeth bearing an uncanny resemblance to those of modern humans. Its muscular arms appear far more powerful than those of a chimpanzee, and while its hands are not unlike yours or mine, its feet are characterized by wide spaces between the big toes and the rest of the toes to aid its climbing capabilities. *Africanus* reaches the ground with a graceful jump from the lowest branches and raises its dark, hairy body to its full height of 1,3 metres before turning around and ambling away with a human-like, yet slightly rolling walk towards the Sterkfontein caves.

TWO MILLION YEARS AGO

Over the past million years the increasing frequency of global ice ages has changed the world significantly. The tropical woodlands that carpeted Africa have retreated into gallery forests clinging to the waterways. Only the equatorial regions remain heavily forested, while to the north and south of the equator the landscape is opening up into savanna and broken woodlands. The food chain has shifted and the entire animal community has changed in response to the encroaching grassland. Almost all the animals that inhabited Africa 1 million years ago have been driven into extinction by the drier conditions. In their place are specialist grazers, ancestors of the modern African animal

forms, many of which evolved in the less lush environments of Asia and Europe and crossed the land bridge into Africa through what is now the Middle East. Among these new invaders are the ancestors of zebra and buffalo, lion and hyena.

At the Cradle of Humankind, the effects of these changes are dramatic. The air feels thinner, less humid, and the great tropical evergreen forest that dominated the valley has receded. The tree belt now barely obscures the river. Even the sky and the clouds appear different. The tropical blueness seems to have been washed out of the sky and the clouds are wispier. The landscape seems quieter. Fewer trees mean that there is not the same level of noise from the chattering profusion of monkeys and birds that inhabited this area half a million years ago. The rushing sound of water has also abated because the river is moving more slowly, which means that the grunts of hippo are sharper and more audible.

The rolling grassland is more expansive, hosting herds of zebra that are as large as Clydesdale carthorses. The closest herd of these giant zebra, *Equus capensis*, is about a hundred strong. They stand still, intently watching the tree line near the river where a group of giant wildebeest-lookalikes, *Megalotragus*, are distinctly jittery, shuffling about before breaking into a run, snorting and shaking their massive horns.

The source of their consternation is a pride of great-maned shaggy lions grouped lazily around the carcass of a zebra on which they have been feeding. Lions, with their co-operative predatory techniques, have replaced the sabre-toothed cats, whose individualistic hunting style was more suited to dense bush than this encroaching African savanna. In both defensive and offensive action, there is safety in numbers on the grassland. The giant savanna baboons, *Theropithecus*, ignore the nearby lions, aware that they have had their fill and will need to rest and digest, while the smaller *Parapapio* baboons watch the activity from the trees.

Moving towards the water's edge is a herd of slender-tusked *Elephas*, too large to worry about the lion. Those that have reached the river are playfully spraying each other with water.

Huddled around a termite mound are two ape-like creatures, a mother and her child. Superficially, they have the same appearance as *Australopithecus africanus*. They are covered in coarse dark hair and have a similar body structure. However, on closer inspection the faces of *Paranthropus robustus* are flatter, larger and more heavily jawed: adaptations to a drier environment.

Whereas *africanus* enjoyed a diet of nuts and berries, the robusts survive on a diet of roots, leaves, grass seeds and bulbs. They need enormous teeth and jaws to crush and grind the tough foods of the savanna. The bigger molars of the robusts have the circumference of a South African 50 cent piece. But they do not subsist on a vegetarian diet only. At the termite mound the mother is using a bone tool to chop into the hard, crusty covering in order to get at the fat white termite larvae that are a handy source of protein in this environment. Her child greedily reaches into the hole to pull out the juicy insects, stopping every now and then to pick up a piece of weathered broken bone to mimic its mother as it learns the art of using tools.

The duo are so intent on consuming this delicacy that they are oblivious to the lions – and to a group of four or five other bipedal creatures that have emerged from the riverine bush and are walking steadily and confidently towards the lions. These hominins are different from the robusts. Although they are not much larger than the paranthropines, their chests are less barrel-like and they walk with more confidence. Their heads are much bigger, yet more refined, without the pronounced jaws of the robusts.

These are habilines, among the first of our own genus, *Homo*. In short, they are more man-ape than ape-man. Their focus is not the big cats, but their kill, the bloody zebra carcass that still has some meat on the bones. The lions, aware of their approach, rise from their languorous positions and circle their kill. The male lion roars a warning, but the hominins do not waver until they are 20 metres away. Then they suddenly start making a big noise, leaping up and down, shouting and brandishing big sticks. This behaviour clearly confuses the lions, who are used to most other animals running away from them.

One of the habilines reaches down and picks up a river cobble from the ground. Holding it in his right hand, he somewhat clumsily casts the rock at the largest male lion, which flinches back from the near miss. Almost immediately all the other man-apes join in the activity and a torrent of stones rains down on the lions, several stones finding their mark. The lions, who had eaten their fill, retreat quickly, disappearing into the thick gallery forest and heading in the direction of Swartkrans, glancing back angrily at the now triumphant man-apes who have claimed their kill and are jumping, hooting and slapping each other in what might be interpreted as a victory dance.

The man-apes approach the carcass. One of them picks up two of the stones that were hurled at the lions, and begins striking them against each other to create a sharp edge on an impromptu stone blade.

The clicking of rocks ends quickly and the members of the small troop gather around the tool maker, pick up small flakes and the large cobble remains and walk over to the carcass. With amazing speed and efficiency they slice the skin with sharp flakes and bash open bones with the larger cobbles to extract the juicy marrow. They exchange sounds in what may, at a stretch of the imagination, be called language rather than animal communication. Some of the individuals pick up pieces of bone and meat and walk off into the woods, maybe carrying food back to their troop.

Back at the termite mound, the robust mother and child have vanished. Disturbed both by the lions and the show of superior technology by the other hominins, they have retreated in the direction of Kromdraai. They are frightened by these aggressive man-apes, who they regard with a mixture of foreboding and familiarity.

ONE MILLION YEARS AGO

The savanna invasion of the gallery forests continues steadily as a consequence of the global cooling of the past 2 million years. The pace of change has slowed down, however, and the landscape of the Cradle of Humankind has changed less dramatically in the past million years. It is beginning to resemble what it will look like in modern times. A summer thundershower builds up in the sky and the jagged ripple of lightning is a reminder that this

area has one of the highest incidences of lightning strikes in the world. Across the valley a tendril of smoke emerges from the Swartkrans Cave and the sudden gust of wind carries with it the smell of burning wood, and something else . . . could it be roasting meat?

At the cave a group of people are huddled around the flickering flames. The confidence and physicality of the *H. habilis* scavenger-hunters have become more pronounced over the last million years and have taken on a purposefulness in these *H. erectus* individuals, who are eating a late lunch of charred giant hyrax. Even in the half-light of the cave it is clear that the *erectus* male is a powerful, muscular creature, more near-human than man-ape. The males stand as tall as modern-day humans, although their broad, somewhat unrefined faces bear traces of their ape-like ancestry.

Where the australopithecines were the hunted, *erectus* is the hunter. He has added the ability to use fire to his expanding tool kit of handaxes and bifaces. Where the australopithecines were specialists in their respective environments, *erectus* is a generalist, able to live in a variety of habitats on a mixed diet of meat and vegetable matter. Unlike the habilines, he is more of a hunter of small mammals than a scavenger, although his skill at driving carnivores off their kills is still a favoured way of obtaining meat in an energetically efficient way. Although wary of the lions' ferocity, he knows that the big cats will lead him to his next meal. Some *erectus* populations are believed to have migrated from Africa to Europe and Asia by following carnivores.

Erectus's dominance over his environment is reinforced by the fact that he is the only hominin to be found in the African landscape. There is no sign of the robusts who coexisted with the genus *Homo* for over a million years. It is likely that they were simply unable to compete with the physical and technical superiority of early *Homo*, who colonized the best camping sites and food-generating areas, gradually marginalizing the robusts to a point where their population growth could not sustain the species.

Away from the cave, in the grassland, it is apparent that there are fewer animals to be seen around the Cradle of Humankind, and those that are visible are far more familiar to someone accustomed to the animals of today. Across the still expanding grassland one can spot the ancestral blesbok *Damaliscus* and the ancient springbok *Antidorcas bondi*, frolicking in the sharp gusts of turbulent air that precede the impending storm.

The giant zebra, *Equus capensis*, now mingles with herds of modern zebra and, for the first time, a warthog appears, tail in the air, trotting briskly through the trees at the edge of the woodland, disturbed from its rooting for tubers by a movement in the trees. A huge hyena emerges. It is *Pachycrocuta brevirostris*, a relative of the spotted hyena and an immigrant from Asia that is at least the size of a female lion. Between its powerful jaws it has the head and horns of a *Megalotragus*, the giant wildebeest, whose carcass it brazenly stole from a young lion still padding hopefully behind the hyena, intimidated by the large thief, but hungry enough not to give up on the kill. In the distance the springboks scatter suddenly as a pack of hunting animals that resemble a cross between a hunting dog and a wolf try to isolate one of the individual antelopes at the edge of the herd.

A crack of lightning and the roll of thunder signal that the rain will soon come. The *erectus* group in the cave watch the approaching storm with interest, particularly the points where lightning strikes, for they know that this is what causes the bush fires, which they have learnt to 'steal' and keep alive in their cave hearths. It is this technology that will allow their descendants to conquer the world.

ONE HUNDRED THOUSAND YEARS AGO

The stone-tipped spear rips through the flank of the giant buffalo *Pelorovis antiquus*, eliciting a resounding bellow of anger, fear and pain as the beast lunges back towards its attackers, trying to skewer them on its impossibly big horns, which measure almost three metres from tip to tip. But the men were anticipating this, and as the raging animal turns, it is speared from the other side. It twists and writhes, its bellowing becoming more panic stricken as its menacing horns become a weighty hindrance, snagged by the thorny shrubs in the grassland. The men sense victory. The *Pelorovis's* front legs buckle as the third spear enters its neck. It sinks to its haunches and collapses, snorting bubbles of blood as one of the hunters steps forward and sinks a two-metre spear into its chest. The nine men shout with delight, dancing triumphantly around the now-motionless *Pelorovis*.

Talking excitedly as they recall the intricate details of the hunt, they waste no time in getting to work on the carcass, stripping off chunks of meat with their sharp stone blades. Their butchery is rapid and systematic, for soon the spotted hyenas (*Crocuta crocuta*) and jackals (*Canis mesomelas*) will arrive, eager to seize what titbits they can.

Already the vultures circle in the sky, waiting for an opportunity to pick the bones clean once the hunters have left. A small pride of lions also watches from the edge of the woodland near the stream, hungry for the buffalo, but clearly wary of the sharp spears of the human hunters.

In the grassland beyond the kill site, in the direction of Sterkfontein, a clearly modern grazing community of antelopes and zebras studiously ignores the drama that has played itself out. Among them are still some remnant giants of the past, such as *Equus capensis* and a small feeding herd of *Megalotragus*, but their numbers are dwindling and within the next 90 thousand years or so, they too will have disappeared from the Earth.

Two of the men are already on their way back to the campsite by the stream, several kilometres away at Plover's Lake, where the women and children have been digging for tubers and roots. One of the other hunters searches around for a medicinal plant to apply to the superficial cut on his arm where the *Pelorovis* horn nicked him as it went down.

The hunters are now as recognizably human as members of our own species, *Homo sapiens*. They are of slighter build than *erectus*, and wear skins around their loins. A running group of women and children emerge from the edge of the river to greet them. They are singing and laughing and calling across the grassland in excitement. It is clear that they belong to the human race as we know it today.

ONE THOUSAND YEARS AGO

The Cradle of Humankind landscape looks just as it does today, obviously with the exception of fences, buildings, lights and power lines. There is an increasing domesticity about the rolling grasslands, which have been occupied by the forebears of the Sotho and Tswana people, migrants from central Africa who came southwards seeking new lands for their cattle and crops. Herds of Nguni cattle now mix with the zebra and antelope that can be seen in the open veld.

Game numbers that had dropped significantly in previous millennia owing to the success of the hunter-gatherers have started picking up again because of the more settled existence of the Iron Age migrants. They are not dependent on hunting for food, although it remains an important part of their social fabric. The newcomers, whose own ancestors first began settling in this area around the 1st century AD, have built their circular wood-thorn enclosures on Coopers Hill, which gives them a vantage point over the surrounding grasslands and is not too far from water. The stone structures, remnants of which still dot the Gauteng highveld, would only be built later. Unlike the hunter-gatherers, who lived close to the river in natural rock overhangs, the Iron Age people build their own settlements, generally dome-shaped, thatched mud-and-daub huts within cattle enclosures, which are surrounded by fields of sorghum. The crops are a staple foodstuff and are also used for brewing beer, which is kept in thick-walled, pinkish pots decorated with hatching and chevron patterns.

The hunter-gatherers and pastoralists are no strangers to one another. They have co-existed for the better part of a thousand years, sometimes fighting, sometimes interacting peacefully. Increasingly, the Iron Age migrants are dominating the area. Their more settled ways have resulted in rapid population growth, and the hunter-gatherers are starting to find themselves incorporated into the new social order, sometimes working as artisans or herders for the newcomers, sometimes trading skins for cattle meat.

Photo taken from the same vantage point as the paintings, overlooking Sterkfontein, Swartkrans, Coopers and Bolt's Farm. (IJ)

The Cradle of Humankind cannot, however, be described as an altogether tamed landscape. Today the cattle herdsmen discuss the drama of the last week, when lions attacked the cattle byres, killing three cows and seizing two calves before nightwatchmen armed with flaming torches and iron-tipped hunting spears drove them back into the darkness. They agree that the 'pendoring' (*Maytenus polyacantha*) byres need to be fortified with more thorny branches. They also discuss the tragedy of a month ago, when a leopard seized a herdboy who had wandered too close to its lair in the dolomite caves at Sterkfontein in search of a stray goat.

Ornaments and decorations have taken on greater significance. Most of the men and women wear copper earrings, necklaces, anklets and bangles made from a variety of materials, showing how important individual body decoration has become.

There are far fewer trees in the area since the arrival of these Iron Age migrants, who have denuded the riverine forests of some of their finest specimens, chopping them down to fuel their hungry furnaces. Producing a single spearhead requires the wood of two large trees and at least two weeks spent collecting the wood, making the charcoal, smelting and furnacing.

It will be more than 800 years before white farmers bring their cattle and fences into the region, and over 900 years before the first palaeontologist begins to search the many caves in these hills for fossils.

CHAPTER *five*

A HOMININ WHO'S WHO

The story of hominin evolution is of course not restricted to southern Africa. It is a pan-African phenomenon that occurred outside the tropical evergreen forests where chimpanzees and gorillas evolved, taking place in the expanding savanna and broken woodland.

It is likely that the cooler climate of the Miocene triggered the evolutionary development of early hominins. Unfortunately very few fossils have been found from between 10 and 6 million years ago, which makes it difficult to establish exactly what creatures gave rise to our earliest ancestors, and what they looked like. The cooler climate led to a shrinking of the primates' familiar environment of the tropical rainforests and this affected their food sources.

Bipedalism is probably a consequence of the destruction of this original forest environment and the encroachment of the savanna grassland. Walking on two legs was also linked to having to travel greater distances for food.

Subsequent climatic changes prompted adaptations to the body shape and brain size of our earliest ancestors. The following section details the earliest hominins, although the exact relationship between them remains speculative (refer also to the diagram on page 20).

Artist John Gurche's reconstruction of an* Australopithecus africanus *family. (NG)

SAHELANTHROPUS TCHADENSIS (7–6 MYA)

The discovery in Chad of a 6 to 7 million-year-old skull of *Sahelanthropus tchadensis*, dubbed the Toumai skull, has stirred debate among anthropologists over whether it is the oldest remnant of a pre-human ancestor or an ancient ape. The Toumai skull was announced by French scientists as the earliest human ancestor in July 2002. The specimen has a thick brow and flat face and strong neck muscle markings. But other scientists say the skull is not on the human branch of the evolutionary tree, but may be that of a female gorilla or a chimpanzee, or a species that has since become extinct. More and better specimens will be required before the debate is settled.

ORRORIN TUGENENSIS (> 6 MYA)

Dubbed the Millennium Man, this hominin was discovered in December 2000 in the Tugen Hills in Kenya's Lake Baringo district by a team led by Brigitte Senut and Martin Pickford. The remains include a femur, pieces of a jaw, some ape-like front teeth, human-like arm bones and a finger bone. Potentially the most dramatic fossil find in the last 20 years, it was designated *Orrorin tugenensis* (Original Man from Tugen).

The Millennium Man is significant because it appears to be over a million years older than any other hominin yet discovered. If this is true, it places the creature at the point in time where the lineage split between ancestral hominins and apes.

Orrorin tugenensis appears to have been a biped with a relatively primitive head, but is unlike any other early hominid because it had ape-like front teeth, yet thickly enamelled, bulbous back teeth very much like those of later hominids.

ARDIPITHECUS RAMIDUS (5,8–4,4 MYA)

The fossil remains of at least 17 individuals of this genus were found in Ethiopia's Afar region by a University of Berkeley, California team led by Tim White and Yohannes Haile-Selassie over a number of field seasons beginning in 1991. The fossils, consisting mostly of teeth, skull pieces and upper limb bones, are highly fragmented, which makes analysis speculative.

The lack of complete lower limb remains means there is still uncertainty about whether *Ardipithecus ramidus* ('the ground ape representing the root') was capable of walking on two legs. White insists that the ankle bone fragments discovered show that it was bipedal, but also comfortable living in trees. Details of the finds have only recently been published, and until the scientific community has time to digest these results, the debate among scientists will continue as to whether this is in fact a hominin or merely an early hominoid, more related to living chimpanzees.

THE AUSTRALOPITHECINES

Between 4 and 1 million years ago, several different species of ape-men inhabited the African landscape. There appears to have been significant regional variation among these species, but two dominant forms have been identified:

- the gracile australopithecines, defined by their relatively 'light' masticating apparatus (their teeth and chewing muscles), an older species that disappeared from the fossil record between 2 and 2,5 million years ago, and
- the robust australopithecines (sometimes placed in the genus *Australopithecus*, but increasingly these days placed in the genus *Paranthropus*), who survived until about 1 million years ago before becoming extinct. They are labelled 'robust' not because of their body size, but because of the tremendous size of their jaws and teeth.

The face of **Australopithecus afarensis,** ***as reconstructed by John Gurche.*** (NG)

The biggest difference between the australopithecines and the chimpanzee-like creatures they are believed to have descended from is that the australopithecines could walk on two legs. The australopithecines also displayed a slight increase in cranial capacity, although they retained a relatively prognathic, or protruding, face.

It has recently become apparent that there were also various postcranial adaptations within the group. Some, for example, were more adapted to climbing, while others were more suited to a terrestrial lifestyle.

Australopithecus anamensis

(4,2–3,8 MYA)

The earliest of the australopithecines, this species is based on a relatively small number of specimens discovered by Meave Leakey's Kenya National Museum team in the Lake Turkana region of Kenya. A large tibia (shin bone) indicates that this species was well adapted to walking on two legs, while the parallel tooth rows visible in the jaws are more ape-like, indicating a very primitive head compared to the hominins listed below. This species looks like a good candidate as ancestor of all later hominins. Towards the end of the Miocene, the shrinking forests of Africa provided less and less habitable space for the apes, and they started to become extinct, a trend that continues today. At the same time, the more terrestrial, faster breeding monkeys began to increase, leading to the dominance of monkeys over apes in terms of numbers.

THE RISE OF PRIMATES

The rise of the primates almost coincides with the end of the dinosaurs 65 million years ago. The dinosaurs are believed to have become extinct when a giant meteorite hit the Gulf of Mexico, resulting in the equivalent of a worldwide nuclear winter that destroyed their food sources.

The first primates were small, tree-shrew-like animals that survived because of their modest food needs. Primates expanded their territory rapidly once the planet's atmosphere regained its equilibrium, filling almost every niche available. This expansion can be attributed to their ability to reproduce rapidly and to control their own body temperature (thermoregulation).

The earliest primates were adapted to a terrestrial, and probably nocturnal lifestyle, but they soon developed diurnal behaviour patterns. Other typical characteristics of primates include their ability to see in three dimensions and suckle their young.

Today, the order Primates is divided into two suborders:

- ♦ the prosimians, which include lemurs, tarsiers and bush-babies, and
- ♦ the anthropoids, which include New and Old World monkeys as well as the living apes and humans.

(G)

The anthropoid line leading to the hominins split during the Oligocene, around 40 million years ago. This led to the Miocene 'heyday' of the apes, beginning about 25 million years ago, when the global tropical climate was conducive to the spread of large-bodied, tail-less apes. During the Middle Miocene, apes spread throughout Africa and into Asia and Europe.

By between 10 and 14 million years ago, the orang-utan group had split from the ancestral hominoid lineage. Between 7 and 9 million years ago, the ancestral lineage of the living gorillas diverged, and the split between the chimpanzee lineage and that of hominins occurred between 5 and 7 million years ago.

Chimpanzees adapted to the tropical evergreen forest and hominins to the more broken woodlands and savannas that were emerging at that time.

Australopithecus afarensis

(3,8–3 MYA)

One of the most widespread of the early hominins and probably the best documented because of the well-known 'Lucy' skeleton, *Australopithecus afarensis* (the southern Ape from Afar) was first discovered by Don Johanson in the Hadar region of Ethiopia in 1973. It was initially believed to be the root ancestor of all subsequent hominins.

More recent discoveries appear to rule this out, although there is an ongoing argument as to where *afarensis* should be placed in the human family tree. Characteristics of this species include sexual dimorphism (the males are larger than the females, much like gorillas), and a cranial capacity of around 400 cubic centimetres. Remains of this species have been found in Tanzania, Ethiopia and possibly Chad.

Although both* afarensis *and* africanus *were bipedal, it is not sure if they walked like modern man, or whether they had a more waddling gait. (NG)

There has been a great deal of debate among scientists as to whether *afarensis* was arboreal or not. Recent discoveries indicate that the species was probably adapted to many different types of habitat. The famous Laetoli footprint trail, in which footprints 3,6 million years old have been preserved in ancient ash near a volcano in Tanzania, is attributed to this species.

Australopithecus africanus

(3,1–2,1 MYA)

The gracile ape-man *africanus* (the southern Ape of Africa) is represented by the fossils of the Taung child and Mrs Ples. This species is slightly more advanced than *afarensis*, with a larger cranial capacity and larger teeth. It is found at sites throughout South Africa and is particularly prevalent at Sterkfontein, but as yet it has not been found elsewhere in Africa.

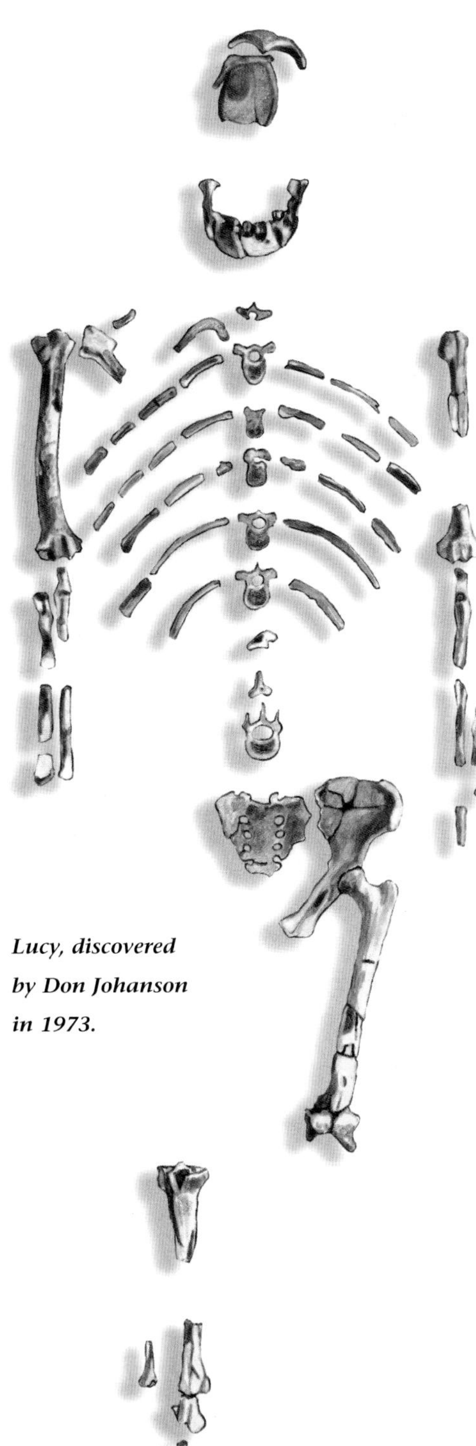

Lucy, discovered by Don Johanson in 1973.

It has been suggested that *africanus* has longer arms and shorter legs than *afarensis*, which at first would suggest that it was more primitive. However, its facial characteristics are much more human-like.

There is inconclusive evidence that *africanus* may have been the mother species for both the robust australopithecines and the early forms of *Homo*.

Australopithecus bahrelghazali

(3,5–3,0 MYA)

This australopithecine was discovered in 1995 in North Africa by French palaeoanthropologist Michel Brunet. It has been suggested that it is a regional variant of *afarensis*. However, only parts of the skull have been found, so very little is known of the rest of the body.

Australopithecus garhi

(2,4 MYA)

The last of the 'definitive' australopithecines, this species is a recent addition to the genus *Australopithecus*. Discovered by Tim White's team in the Middle Awash region of Ethiopia, *garhi* appears to be more advanced than *afarensis*, displaying a mixture of both gracile and robust tendencies. Named after the Afar word for surprise, *garhi* has been found in association with stone tools, but there is no evidence yet that it was capable of making tools. Fragmentary postcranial evidence suggests that *garhi* had both long arms and long legs, giving it unusual body proportions compared to other early hominins.

PARANTHROPUS (2,5–1,0 MYA)

Formerly classified as a robust form of *Australopithecus* but now more frequently put into the separate genus *Paranthropus*. *Paranthropus* fossils are characterized by massive teeth and jaw muscles, which indicate a low-nutrition vegetarian diet (lots of chewing to extract nutrients) that may have been an adaptation to the drier African environment 3 million years ago. Recent examinations of its hand bones have revealed that *Paranthropus* had the capability to manufacture and manipulate stone tools, which are often found in association with fossil remains. However, there is still no definitive evidence that *Paranthropus* or *Homo* made the tools found in the fossil sites in the Cradle of Humankind. *Paranthropus* had a relatively smaller brain than contemporaneous hominins in the genus *Homo*, but a slightly larger brain than the gracile australopithecines.

Australopithecus africanus *foraged in trees, and may also have sought cover among the branches from predators.* (NG)

Paranthropus aethiopicus

(2,6–2,2 MYA)

Found in Kenya and Ethiopia, *aethiopicus* is suspected to be the common ancestor of the later paranthropines. The Black Skull, discovered in Kenya by Alan Walker in 1985, is the best fossil example of this species. It is the first species in the hominin fossil record to exhibit the massive teeth and chewing muscles that characterize the shift to a vegetarian lifestyle brought about by the aridification of Africa and the disappearance of the Miocene forests.

Paranthropus boisei

(2,2–1,2 MYA)

Producing some of the largest fossil representatives of the robust australopithecines, *boisei* epitomizes a 'hyper-robust' ape-man. With their huge teeth and massive jaws, males of this species are unmistakable, typically having bony crests atop their skulls just to support their massive jaw muscles. Relative to body size, they have the smallest hominin brain case recorded (less than 420 cc), although some individuals have cranial capacities in the low 500 cc range. The best known example is the 'Nutcracker Man' discovered by Mary and Louis Leakey at Olduvai Gorge in Tanzania in 1959 and given this name by Phillip Tobias. This specimen was also often referred to as 'Dear Boy', a play on the name *boisei*.

Paranthropus robustus

(2,0–1,0 MYA)

Robustus is the southern African version of the robust ape-men. Often called the flat-faced ape-man because of its dished-out facial area, it is the most common hominin in southern Africa

SK48 (**P. robustus*****), found at Swartkrans in 1948.*** (GG)

WHO WERE THE FIRST TOOL MAKERS?

One of the most difficult questions facing scientists trying to interpret the behaviour of early hominins is: who made the tools found at the sites?

It had always been presumed that members of the genus *Homo*, with their bigger brains and more human-like bodies, were the makers of the stone and bone tools found at sites both in southern and East Africa.

However, recent work on the morphology of the robust australopithecines, and increasing discoveries of these more 'primitive' hominins in direct association with tools, mean that the robust ape-men cannot be excluded as possible tool users and makers.

Nevertheless, with no direct way of linking any single species to the tools recovered with their remains, and considering that practically every site in the right time range contains both *Homo* and *Paranthropus* remains, scientists are still a long way from discovering exactly which hominin made which tool.

and probably the best represented fossil hominin in the African record. The first robust australopithecine was discovered by Robert Broom at Kromdraai in 1938. Since then, fossil remnants have been found at Swartkrans, Drimolen, Kromdraai, Coopers and Gondolin.

EARLY HOMO (2,4–1,8 MYA)

The key difference between the australopithecines and the lumped group 'early *Homo*' is that the latter had a much larger and more complex brain that may be linked to tool making abilities. Typically, we characterize early *Homo* by its more generalized skull, with no specialized adaptations such as sagittal crests or a flattened face. *Homo* species had less prominent brow ridges and a general reduction in facial prognathism. Early *Homo* species had smaller pre-molars and seemed to be omnivorous, adding substantially more meat to their diet than the mainly vegetarian australopithecines.

The earliest known fossil specimens have been dated to around 2,4 mya, and show generalized characteristics. They are found throughout Africa, and many have not been classified to species. *Homo habilis* and *H. rudolfensis* are two later types of 'confirmed' early *Homo* species, but even their status is sometimes questioned, with some palaeo-anthropologists wanting to place them in the genus *Australopithecus*. In South Africa, early *Homo* fossils have been found at Sterkfontein, Coopers, Swartkrans and Drimolen.

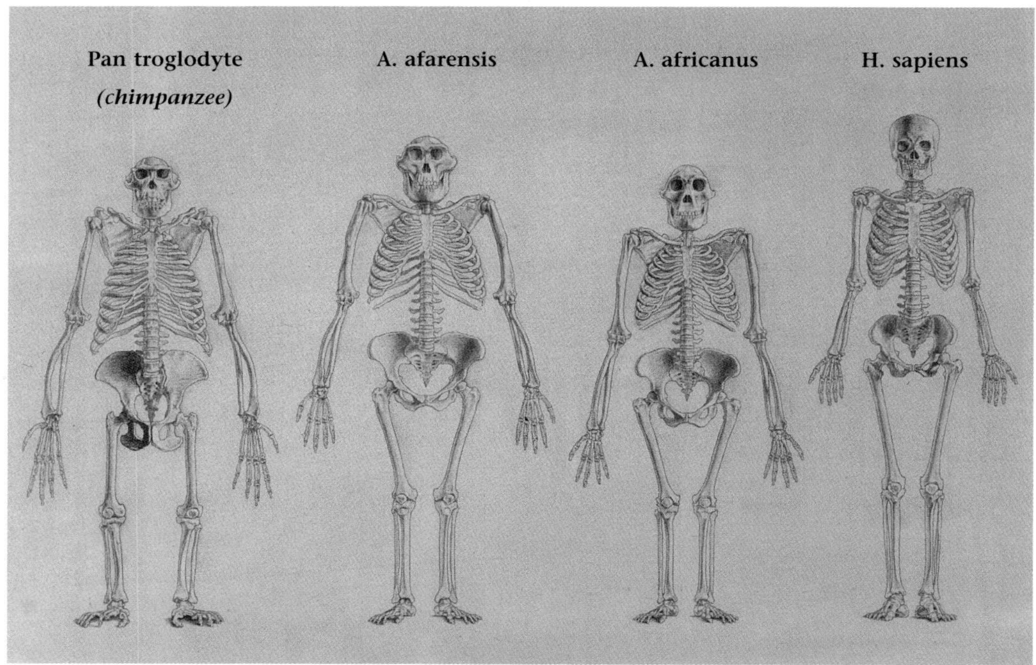

(NG)

LUMPERS VS. SPLITTERS

One of the problems in tracing the development of a new species is the gradation that takes place in between the definite changes of physical characteristics. It is therefore often difficult to decide on which side of the dividing line a species may be, or exactly where that dividing line lies. This is one of the problems faced by scientists categorizing hominins during the 3- to 2-million-year period when several species co-existed.

The debate around early *Homo* is particularly vociferous in this regard. Some scientists argue that *Homo habilis*, the much heralded 'first human' considered to have been the original maker of stone tools, was actually an australopithecine, and that a more correct appellation would be *Australopithecus habilis.*

The argument as to who falls in the genus *Homo* or not usually revolves around brain size, with 650 cc being the generally accepted dividing line. However, the more discoveries that are made, the more arbitrary this definition appears to be.

Because of the degree of variation among the early species of *Homo* discovered so far, scientists generally fall into one of two camps in their definitions:

- The lumpers – those who group *Homo* into three broad categories (*habilis, erectus* and *sapiens*) and downplay the significance of the variations within these categories, often by ascribing them to regional tendencies.
- The splitters – scientists who believe the variations are significant enough to warrant new species within the genus *Homo*, and that the fossil record so far indicates that early *Homo* consisted of a number of species (*habilis, rudolfensis, ergaster, erectus*).

The jury is still out on which approach is better. The only thing known for sure is that the record of early humanity is far more complicated than previously thought.

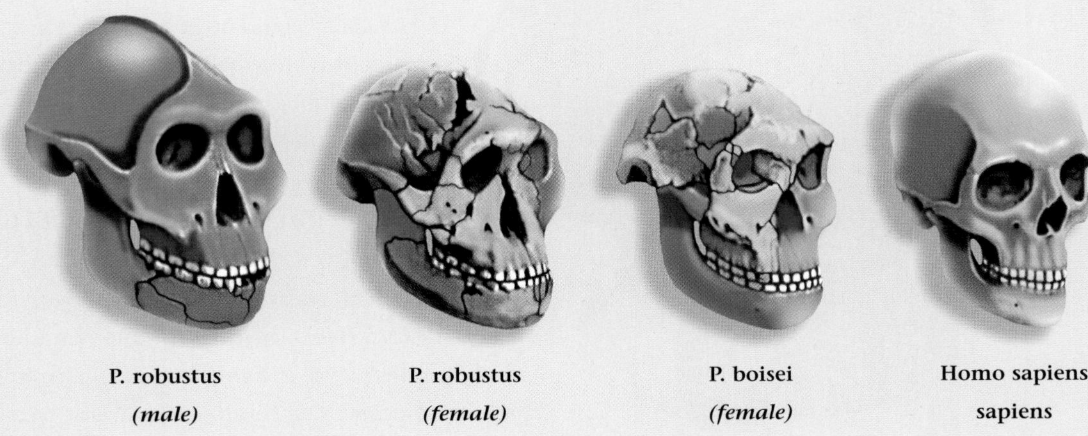

P. robustus *(male)* | P. robustus *(female)* | P. boisei *(female)* | Homo sapiens sapiens

Homo rudolfensis

(EST. 2,4–1,8 MYA)

Rudolfensis was named after Lake Rudolph, the colonial name for Lake Turkana, where its fossilized remains were found by Richard Leakey in the late 1960s and early 1970s.

The argument for *rudolfensis* as a separate species is a tenuous one because of the lack of strong fossil evidence. Indeed, some scientists have rather unkindly described *rudolfensis* as a garbage-can species, consisting of all the 'throwaway' bits of fossils that can't be neatly ascribed to *habilis* or *ergaster*. It has affinities with many of the hominins, including *Homo habilis*, *H. ergaster* and *H. erectus*. It has been tentatively associated with simple flake tool technology. It is hypothesized that *H. rudolfensis* congregated near areas that offered many different food resources, such as lake margins, stream confluences and hills.

Homo habilis

(2–1,6 MYA)

With a larger brain than the australopithecines (around 650–800 cc), *Homo habilis*, meaning 'handy man', is the earliest species of hominin placed in the genus *Homo*. The first specimen was found by the Leakeys at Olduvai Gorge in 1960. The species is characterized by a rounder head, reduced prognathism, more human-like teeth and less pronounced brow ridges.

Habilis has long been associated with the crude Oldowan tool industry. Based on a very fragmentary skeleton from Olduvai Gorge in Tanzania, it has been suggested that *H. habilis* had long arms and short legs. This characteristic suggests that fossils attributed to *H. habilis* would be better placed in the genus *Australopithecus*, thus creating some doubt as to whether *habilis* was in fact the ancestor of *erectus*.

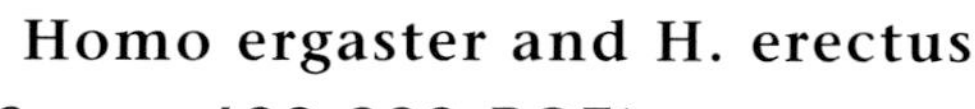

Homo ergaster and H. erectus

(2 MYA–400 000 BCE)

Homo ergaster is often used as a synonym for 'early African *Homo erectus*'. Around 2 million years ago, there was a dramatic shift in hominin cranial and postcranial morphology. *Homo erectus* can be regarded as the first easily identifiable true

Homo rudolfensis.

human ancestor. Reaching modern human stature, but with a brain approximately three-quarters the size of a modern human brain, the earliest *H. erectus* must have been a formidable creature on the African savanna.

The technology of *H. erectus* is epitomized by the handaxe, a generally enormous, teardrop-shaped bifacial tool. *Homo erectus* is the first hominin known to have left Africa. It developed the controlled use of fire, although the only evidence of this in Africa thus far can be found at Swartkrans in the Cradle of Humankind. By 700 000 to 1 million years ago, *erectus* was distributed throughout the Old World.

The face of* H. erectus *as reconstructed by John Gurche. (NG)

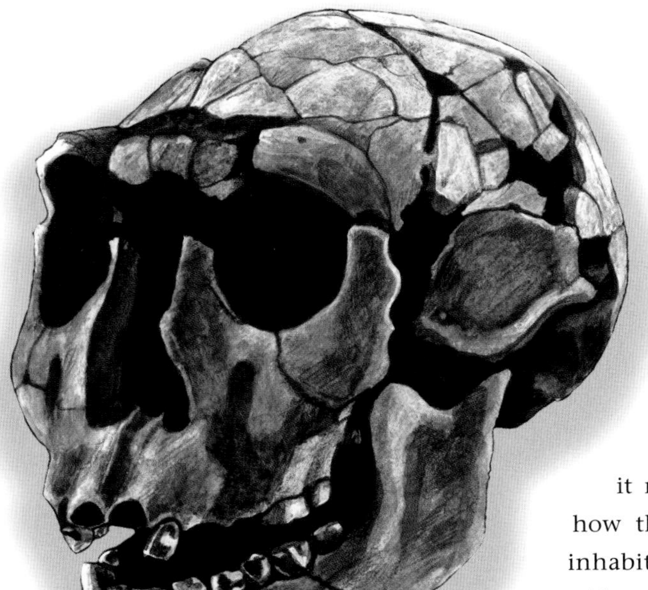

This* Homo erectus *skull of a boy from Nariokotome, Kenya, is part of one of the most complete hominin skeletons recovered to date.

It is now even suggested that in Indonesia, *H. erectus* developed some level of sea-faring or rafting capabilities that enabled them to travel between islands. To this day it remains something of a mystery as to how the Indonesian islands were originally inhabited by early *H. erectus*. Stone tool evidence from islands that were never connected by land bridges indicates that these remote archipelagos were occupied. *H. erectus* must have either swum, rafted or boated across the waters to reach these islands. What could have motivated them to undertake such a perilous step into the unknown is a matter of speculation.

STONE TOOLS – THE DAWN OF TECHNOLOGY

The earliest stone tools discovered so far are from the Gona area in Ethiopia, and are believed to date back to approximately 2,5 million years ago. The appearance of stone tools has been linked to the development of our own genus, *Homo*. However, the Gona tools predate by 100 000 years the earliest *Homo* specimens found so far, which suggests either that an earlier form of *Homo* still remains to be found, or that the australopithecines like *Australopithecus garhi* were capable of making stone tools.

Stone tools are categorized into 'cultures' depending on how they were made or used. The basic categories are:

An example of Middle Stone-aged flake technology.

- Oldowan – a crude and limited stone tool kit associated with the Early Stone Age, and named after the Olduvai Gorge site in Tanzania where the first examples were found.
- Acheulian – a more refined and complicated tool kit that developed during the Early Stone Age (1,6 mya) and lasted until approximately 250 000 years ago, named after the French site of Saint Acheul.
- Later Stone Age – this continued in Africa far longer than it did in Europe; these tools are more specialized and more diverse than the earlier tool technologies.

The Cradle of Humankind contains a representative sample of almost all stone tool types manufactured by humans and their ancestors over the last 2 million years in Africa.

The Oldowan tools found in the Cradle of Humankind date back to approximately 2 million years ago and have been found at sites such as Sterkfontein Member 5 and recently at the Coopers site. These tools are really just flakes, the result of reducing a large stone to a smaller stone, and show little if any control over the end design. Included in the Oldowan culture are simple hammerstones, which may have been nothing more than readily available river cobbles.

The more advanced tools of the Acheulian industry have been found at Swartkrans, and in the river gravels around the Cradle Nature Reserve. They are believed to date back to approximately 1,5 million years ago. The core element of the Acheulian tool kit is the handaxe. This bifacial, teardrop-shaped tool was the early Pleistocene equivalent of the Swiss Army knife, and was used for just about any task *Homo erectus*, the presumed maker of the Acheulian industry, might have wished to accomplish.

The Acheulian industry shows that deliberate choice was introduced into the tool-making process, from the raw material to the 'style' of the end product. It is the most enduring tool culture in history, existing for well over a million years with little variation. The same templates have been found across the world, from Africa to Europe and Asia. The Acheulian ended only about 250 000 years ago, which may be associated with the rise of archaic *H. sapiens* who, with a bigger brain size and more developed communication skills, developed a new kind of tool industry.

At sites such as Swartkrans and Plover's Lake, one can see evidence of flake industries and prepared core industries. This is a period that is termed the 'Middle Stone Age' in southern Africa. Points and blades began to appear and some of the finely crafted stone tools were hafted on to spears. In the coastal regions of southern Africa, new evidence is emerging that the Middle Stone Age was characterized by a technological complexity never before realised, with bone points and even artwork appearing contemporaneously with what used to be considered 'primitive' human technologies.

The timing of the transition from Middle Stone Age to Later Stone Age is complex, with evidence that in some areas 'modern' complex tools and culture appeared very early, while in other areas the transition from Middle Stone Age behaviour to the modern 'infinite' tool kit and behaviour may have occurred as recently as 20 000 years ago. Early and Middle Stone Age tools were characterized by their limitations – they were used essentially for bludgeoning, scraping, and cutting. The evolution of modern human behaviour saw the emergence of a far more complex tool kit, with stone, bone and wooden tools having an infinite variety of uses, from stitching clothing to harpooning fish. Later Stone Age tools were also influenced by an aestheticism that was not prevalent in early tool cultures, reflecting the increasing sophistication of evolving human interaction. Later Stone Age tools used by the San hunter-gatherers are microlithic and far more specialized than Early and Middle Stone Age tools.

The evidence for Later Stone Age occupation of the Cradle of Humankind is extensive. Almost every cave has some evidence of modern human occupation, and microlithic tools are widespread.

Examples of stone tools from the Later Stone Age.

Homo antecessor

(1,0 MYA–800 000 BCE)

This variation of early *Homo* is restricted to southern Europe and possibly North Africa. *Antecessor* had a relatively 'modern' looking face, but with features of *erectus* in the cranium and later Neanderthals in the nasal region. It had a cranial capacity of around 1 000 cc. *Homo antecessor* is a good candidate ancestor of *H. heidelbergensis* and then *H. neanderthalensis*. Its remains have been found at La Sima de los Huesos, near Atapuerca in Northern Spain, preserved in a deep cave. The bodies of at least six individuals may have been deposited there in ritual burial.

Homo heidelbergensis

(600 000–200 000 BCE)

As tall as or even taller than modern humans and more robustly built, *Homo heidelbergensis* was probably the precursor of the Neanderthals in Europe, and the possible ancestor of *H. sapiens* in Africa. Archaeological evidence shows that this species was capable of group-hunting large game. Scrape marks on bones, indicating de-fleshing, may be a sign of cannibalism. There is a great deal of confusion as to whether the large robust human fossils found in Africa from this time period are members of this species or something different. Very large human remains have been found in southern Africa that have tentatively been attributed to *H. heidelbergensis*. These remains are mostly from the Cape coast.

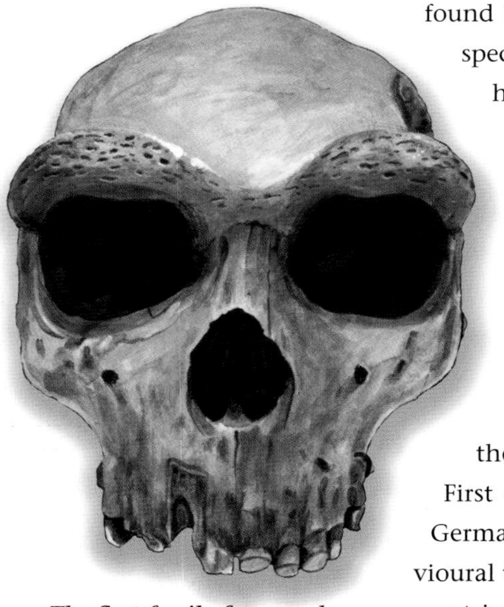

The first fossil of any early human ancestor to be found in Africa, this skull of **H. heidelbergensis** *was discovered in Kabwe in 1921.*

Homo neanderthalensis

(230 000–29 000 BCE)

Neanderthals appear to have evolved out of *Homo antecessor*, and were adapted to living in very cold climates. Their bodies were stocky and their nasal passages were adapted for processing icy air. First discovered in 1856 in the Neander Tal (valley) in Germany, Neanderthals shared many cultural and behavioural traits with modern humans. They seem to have been restricted initially to Europe, where they survived a series of ice ages over the last several hundred thousand years. However, it appears that later adaptations allowed them to live in temperate climates. Their remains have also been found in the Middle East, Asia and North Africa.

NEANDERTHALS AND HUMANS

Of all the hominins, the Neanderthals are probably the species that has most captured the imagination of modern humans. Although generally thought of as lumbering brutes, research does not support this. Neanderthal brains were, on average, actually larger than those of modern humans, with whom they co-existed for at least 50 000 years. Whether or not the two species could communicate or even mate is not known.

Like *H. heidelbergensis*, it is believed that Neanderthals used their front teeth to hold objects while working with tools. They employed a sophisticated tool technology known as the Mousterian, a stone tool industry characterized by flakes chipped into points, burins (chisels), borers for skins, and drills. They had no fine points or blade technologies. Neanderthals are known to have used wooden spears for stabbing and thrusting, but not for throwing.

The only known object of 'art' attributable to Neanderthals has been found in Hungary – a single carved, polished baby mammoth tooth, etched and covered with red ochre, dated to around 80 000 years before the present.

However, the presence of jewellery made of antler and bone alongside Neanderthal remains indicates efforts by modern humans to trade with Neanderthals. A flute has also been discovered in association with Neanderthal remains, dating to around 50 000 years ago and possessing the seven-note diatonic scale of modern music.

A Neanderthal grave in Shanidar, Iraq, contained the remains of four individuals, a man, two women and an infant, and the pollen of spring flowers. The pollen could be an indication of early burial practices, or merely the result of droppings from burrowing rodents.

Neanderthals went extinct about 25 000 years ago in the face of expanding populations of modern humans. It would appear that they did not have the intellectual or psychological resources to compete with modern humans, whose superior communication skills and brain power put them in a position of dominance in the utilization of food sources. Over time, this would have affected the reproduction rate of the Neanderthals and, unable to maintain viable population levels, they slowly moved towards extinction.

Neanderthal man as reconstructed by John Gurche. (NG)

OUT OF AFRICA

Africa gave the world humankind. It is scientifically uncontested that the earliest hominins developed in Africa and that *Homo erectus* led the first wave of migrations into the rest of the world approximately 1,8 million years ago. *Erectus* populations soon established themselves in most of the habitable areas in Europe and Asia.

There are two main schools of thought as to how modern humans originated:

- The multi-regional hypothesis holds that *H. sapiens sapiens* evolved regionally from the *erectus* populations distributed throughout the world. The implication is that Chinese *H. sapiens* had a fundamentally different origin from African *H. sapiens* and that differences between people are more biologically than culturally entrenched.
- The out-of-Africa hypothesis postulates that *H. sapiens* developed in Africa and then migrated from the continent, gradually replacing *H. erectus* populations in the rest of the world because of their superior technology and communication skills.

Modern genetic research increasingly supports the out-of-Africa hypothesis, showing that there is a greater genetic diversity among Africans than between Africans and other populations. Fundamentally, this means that Africans are 'older' and other race groups 'younger'. Geneticists believe that we are all descended from a population of modern *H. sapiens* that lived somewhere in Africa approximately 100 000 years ago.

Archaeological evidence suggests that an 'African Eve' lived in southern Africa. Nowhere else in the world is there a comparable record of evolutionary development demonstrating how *H. erectus* evolved into an archaic form of *H. sapiens*, which became refined into modern *H. sapiens.*

One of the plausible theories on the origin of modern humans is that a sustainable population of archaic *sapiens* was cut off from the African interior by the expansion of the Kalahari and Karoo deserts around 200 000 years ago. This group found itself trapped in the narrow coastal plains between the Atlantic and the mountains on the edge of the desert. This is why their food consumption became increasingly marine-focused. Their diet of shellfish, mussels and fish, with its high protein levels, may have contributed to the development of the modern human brain.

Homo sapiens

(200 000 YEARS AGO TO PRESENT)

Genetic evidence and the fossil record point to an African origin for modern humans. Modern *Homo sapiens* appears to have evolved from an archaic form that in turn evolved from *H. erectus*. Genetic evidence from examinations of both mitochondrial DNA (from the female line) and Y chromosome DNA (from the male line) adds support to the hypothesis that modern humans arose in Africa between 100 000 and 200 000 years ago. Modern

(NG)

humans reached Europe and, via coastal routes, Indonesia and Australia, by around 50 000–60 000 years ago. Until recently, it was believed that modern human behaviour, characterized by the production of art, the burial of the dead and a complex tool kit, was a relatively recent, European phenomenon attributable only to Cro-Magnon man (an early type of *H. sapiens*) around 25 000–35 000 years ago. However, recent discoveries in Africa suggest that the earliest evidence of all these 'modern' attributes can be found in coastal sites and sites in East Africa more than 100 000 years earlier.

FOSSIL SITES

In December 1998, the United Nations declared the fossil sites of the Cradle of Humankind a World Heritage Site. These sites exist within an area of mixed land use. Land owners are working together to develop it as a tourist attraction and ensure that it is protected for future generations.

There are 13 major fossil sites in the Cradle of Humankind, some of which are internationally renowned, such as the Sterkfontein caves, but most of which are relatively unknown, such as the newer sites of Coopers and Gondolin. Not all the sites are accessible to the public, and one should refer to the information section at the back of the book for details on how to visit the sites listed below.

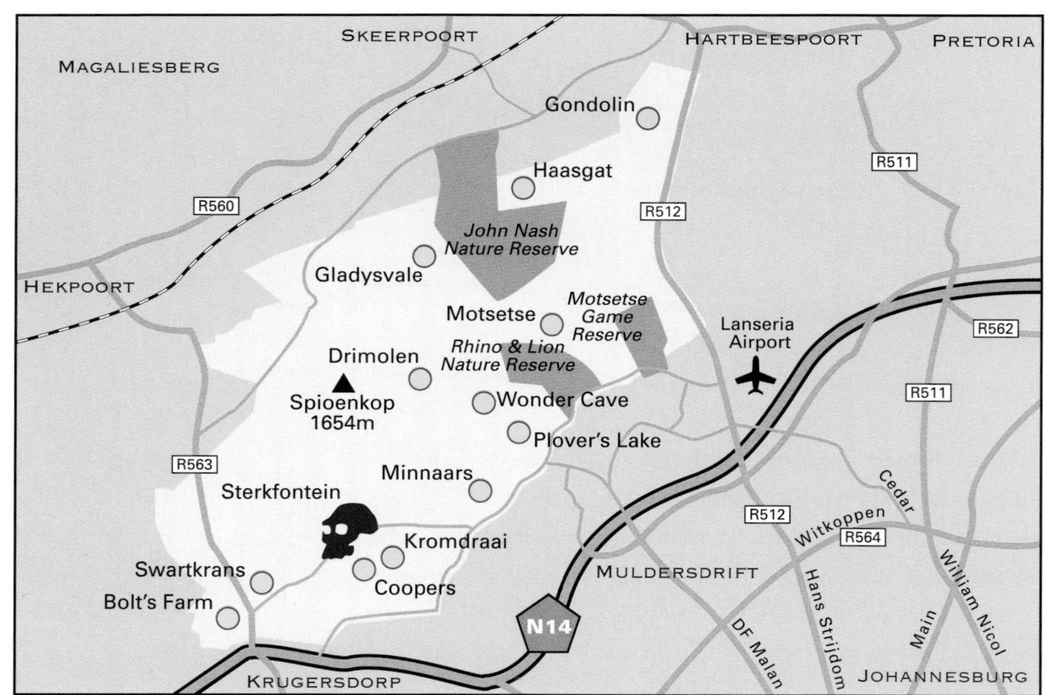

An aerial view of Sterkfontein. (NL)

STERKFONTEIN

Sterkfontein is the site of one of the world's longest running archaeological digs, having been continuously excavated since 1966. Discovered in 1896 by prospectors excavating for lime, it was soon apparent that the site not only housed an incredibly beautiful series of caverns, including one with an underground lake, but that it was also rich in fossil material. In 1897, geologist David Draper succeeded in preventing the lime-workers from doing any further damage to the main cavern, although the lime-mining operations continued on the hillside around the cave, probably destroying many valuable fossils in the process.

Only in 1935 was the true palaeontological value of Sterkfontein revealed when Trevor Jones discovered a number of monkey fossils there. In 1936 this came to the attention of two of Raymond Dart's students, GWH Schepers and H le Riche, who alerted the famous fossil finder Robert Broom to the number of fossils found there. Shortly thereafter, Robert Broom visited the cave and found that the chief quarryman, GW Barlow, had worked at Taung

Robert Broom. (SIL)

Excavations at the Sterkfontein caves. (SIL)

when the Taung child was discovered and knew what kind of specimens Broom was looking for. Shortly thereafter, Barlow produced for Broom a natural brain endocast of an adult australopithecine. In 1938 Broom named this *Plesianthropus transvaalensis* (Near Man from the Transvaal), but with later consolidation of classification, mainly by John Robinson, it was reassigned to *Australopithecus africanus*.

The next major find at Sterkfontein was the now famous Mrs Ples (Sts 5), which was blasted out of the breccia in somewhat controversial circumstances. Broom had been banned from using dynamite to extract fossils because there was no guarantee that the specimens he was trying to dislodge would survive intact. He managed to enlist the support of the then prime minister, Jan Smuts, in overturning the ban imposed by the National Monuments Council, and within a few days successfully dynamited an australopithecine skull from Sterkfontein. Mrs Ples proved to the world that, had the Taung child grown up, it would definitely not have been an ape, but rather of a species intermediate between apes and humans.

Sterkfontein fell on hard times in the 1950s owing to a lack of finds and funding, but was saved yet again, this time by Professor Phillip Tobias and his colleagues at the University of the Witwatersrand. In 1966 the Stegman family donated the site to Wits, which facilitated the opening of the rather modest Robert Broom Museum near the mouth of the caves, and secured funding that enabled Sterkfontein to become the world's longest running uninterrupted archaeological dig. Alun Hughes, first site supervisor, had a thankless job for many years because of the lack of interesting fossil finds emerging from Sterkfontein.

Sterkfontein caves. (SIL)

THE SPECIATION WINDOW

Making sense of the hominins from Sterkfontein has always been difficult, in large part because of the difficulty of dating them accurately. Part of the problem is that the stratigraphy (the distinct layers in which rock is arranged) of the caves appears so jumbled because of water erosion and cave infills. The other complication is the degree of physical variation in specimens ascribed to *Australopithecus africanus*. This has made the contextualization of fossils an arduous and often controversial task.

Despite this there is intriguing evidence that a speciation event might have unfolded at Sterkfontein between 2,6 and 2,8 million years ago. Speciation is the process in which one species starts taking on the physical characteristics that will eventually lead to the evolution of a different species altogether. In 1990 Ron Clarke caused something of a controversy when he stated that the hominin samples he had been studying from Member 4 of Sterkfontein appeared to represent the beginning of this speciation event. He suggested that the range of *africanus* material from Sterkfontein was too great to be ascribed to either a single species, or to males and females within that species. He based his argument on a single specimen, Stw 252, which he said appeared to be derived (eroded from an older sediment and redeposited in a younger sediment) and thus older than most of the ape-men fossils excavated from the site.

Initially, Phillip Tobias vigorously rejected Clarke's argument, pointing out – with some justification – that Clarke had chosen a particularly damaged specimen in Stw 252 upon which to base such a sweeping statement. Tobias also pointed out that Clarke had only used a few morphological traits to make his case and had no statistics to back his argument. Clarke conceded that there was a level of subjective interpretation in reconstructing the skull, but insisted that the teeth, which were in relatively good condition, were far larger than the accepted norm in the gracile ape-men.

Recent work by Charles Lockwood, working on skulls, and Jacopo Moggi-Cechi, working on teeth, supports the idea that there are two, or even more, species of hominin in Sterkfontein Member 4.

Whether or not the speciation event will be proved remains to be seen. However, it would appear that if there was a speciation event at Sterkfontein, it could have represented *africanus* taking on the characteristics not only of early *Homo*, but also of the robust australopithecines.

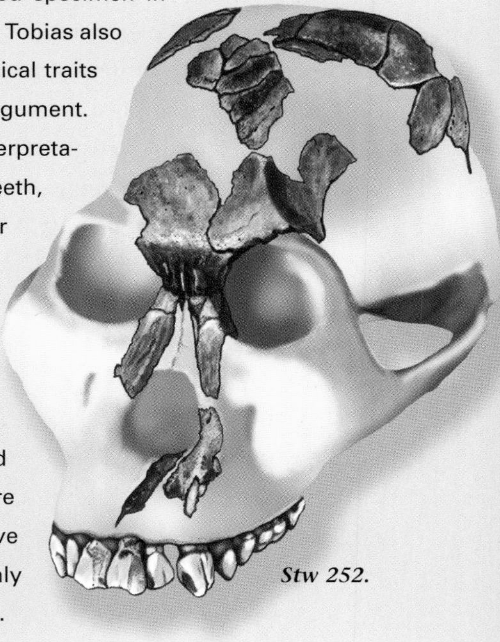

Stw 252.

This changed in 1976 with the discovery of a new hominin – the first reported *Homo habilis* to be unearthed in South Africa. By the end of the 1980s Tobias and Hughes had amassed some 500 hominin fossils from Sterkfontein, as well as thousands of other faunal and floral remains.

Ron Clarke took over the supervision of Sterkfontein after the death of Hughes in 1992. In 1994 he discovered the foot bones of a hominin that had been overlooked during earlier excavations. This specimen, designated Stw 573, became known in the press as 'Little Foot'. In 1997 Clarke's team found the rest of the Little Foot skeleton in the Silberberg Grotto in Member 2. At the time of going to press the fossil was still being extracted from Sterkfontein and had not yet been described, nor has its exact age yet been determined.

SWARTKRANS

Like many of the sites in the Cradle of Humankind, Swartkrans was heavily mined for lime during the 1930s. Broom and Robinson moved their field team from Sterkfontein to Swartkrans in 1948 and blasted breccia from close to the crest of the Swartkrans hill. This was richly fossiliferous and immediately yielded remains of a hominin that Broom described as *Paranthropus crassidens*, regarding it as a different hominin species from the one found earlier at Kromdraai. During the subsequent months many valuable finds were made, including the jaw of an early form of *Homo* by John Robinson in April 1949. This was the first recorded co-existence of *Homo* and the robust australopithecines, an important discovery later to be confirmed in East Africa.

Excavations continued through 1949 until financial problems brought work to a halt. Lime-workers then blasted there throughout 1950 and 1951, much to the consternation of palaeontologists, but this resulted in the discovery of some spectacular specimens such as Sk 48, a *robustus* cranium, and the mandible Sk 23.

The holes in this juvenile hominin skull from Swartkrans exactly match the canines of a fossil leopard. (GG)

An exterior view of the Swartkrans Cave. (IJ)

After Broom died in 1951, Robinson managed to recommence work at Swartkrans, continuing until 1953. The site was then abandoned for 12 years, although active research was carried out during this time at the Transvaal Museum on various aspects of the fauna and geology of Swartkrans and other Sterkfontein Valley caves.

When Bob Brain was appointed palaeontologist at the Transvaal Museum in 1965, he started a field project at Swartkrans that ran without interruption for 21 years. In 1967 the site was purchased by Wits University, but work continued under the stewardship of Brain and the Transvaal Museum. At this time work started on the site where extensive lime-mining was done in earlier decades. It took seven years to systematically remove the miners' rubble, during which time a wealth of fossils came to light, including specimens of *Homo* and stone tools that were studied by Mary Leakey. The subsequent 14 years were devoted to the systematic excavation of the natural overburden and underlying cave deposits. It became apparent that the cave was much more extensive than had previously been thought, and it was discovered that most of the fossils from the Broom-Robinson era had come from an isolated block of breccia clinging to the cave's north wall, a feature that became known as the Hanging Remnant. This has proved to be the key to understanding the cave's stratigraphy.

THE ROBUSTS AND BONE TOOLS

In 1998 Wits graduate student Lucinda Backwell came to some interesting conclusions about the use of bone tools by robust australopithecines. Working with French scientist Francesco d'Errico, she made an intensive study of the scratch marks on bones found at Swartkrans to find out what had caused them. She compared data on 40 different accumulation agents, from animals such as hyena and porcupines, to that of natural agents such as water and weathering, and in the process studied tens of thousands of bones. However, the scratch patterns on the Swartkrans bones, which radiated from the bone tips, were unique, unlike any of the other specimens studied. One day Backwell noticed that there were a number of termite mounds around the Swartkrans Cave and in an inspirational flash recalled a study done on chimpanzees in central Africa. The chimps had been observed sticking twigs into termite mounds, pulling them out full of nutritionally rich termites and then eating them off the sticks. She and D'Errico fashioned their own bone tools and stuck them into the hard crusts of the termite mounds to get at the insects. They then studied the scratch marks on the bones underneath a microscope and found that they were identical to those on the Swartkrans bone tools. This shows that the robust australopithecines had the mental capacity to fashion bone tools and use them to gather food. Could they not therefore have made stone tools as well? If that is the case, the traditional view that our genus *Homo* distinguished itself from its hominin predecessors by the ability to make tools is incorrect. The ape-men may therefore have been more sophisticated than has been thought up until now.

Some of the tools found at Swartkrans, like this bone point, may be up to 2 million years old.

An antelope horn core with criss-cross striations near the tip that prove it was used as a digging stick.

Possibly the greatest contribution of Swartkrans, however, has been the discovery by Brain of the earliest controlled use of fire. In a careful analysis of over 250 burnt bones from the site, Brain established that the remains were burnt in a hearth that had been maintained over many years, making this the earliest evidence for the controlled use of energy by humans nearly 1 million years ago. Evidence of the use of fire elsewhere in the world has only been dated back to about 500 000 years ago.

KROMDRAAI

Fossil hominins were first discovered at Kromdraai by a boy named Gert Terreblanche and described by Robert Broom in 1938. This was the first discovery of a robust australopithecine (TM1517) in the world. Excavations immediately after this discovery yielded disappointingly little. Renewed excavations began in 1941 at the Kromdraai B site and a juvenile robust australopithecine mandible was found, but little else. Broom then turned his attention to Sterkfontein, but in 1944 sent his son, Leonard, to sort through the tailings at Kromdraai. Leonard discovered a lower mandible that fitted the palate of TM1517. In 1947 Broom began intensive work at Kromdraai A, 40 metres from B, hoping to obtain a more extensive faunal assemblage in order to contextualize the hominin finds. Although a large sample of fossil animals was discovered, there were no hominin remains. In March 1955 Bob Brain renewed work at Kromdraai, initiating the first detailed examination of the geology, stratigraphy and taphonomy of the site. From 1977 to 1980 Elizabeth Vrba and Tim Partridge made an intensive geological study of the area. During these three years they found numerous animal fossils, but only five hominin fossils. In 1993 field work began there again under Lee Berger of Wits University and Francis Thackeray of the Transvaal Museum, assisted by Wits graduate student Colin Menter. In 1997 Thackeray discovered stone tools in the *in situ* breccia of Kromdraai A, the first definitive evidence of hominin activity in this part of the deposit.

Kromdraai A, where tools believed to be at least 1 million years old have been found. (IJ)

Kromdraai, where the first robust australopithecine was found. (IJ)

COOPERS

Coopers, located midway between Sterkfontein and Kromdraai, is one of the most interesting of the 'new' sites. It was first discovered in the mid-1930s, when a lecturer from the University of the Witwatersrand named Middleton-Shaw reported the discovery of a single hominin tooth at the site after a field trip to Sterkfontein. He and his students had walked across to Kromdraai after a tour of Sterkfontein, stumbled across the Coopers dumps and found the block of breccia containing the tooth. As happens quite often, controversy erupted over the find. An accusation was even made that the tooth had been taken from Sterkfontein by one of the students! This tooth was housed in the Wits dental school, and was lost sometime in the 1960s or 1970s. Only a single plaster cast remains.

In the 1950s, as part of his PhD thesis work, Bob Brain collected a small amount of material from the only good exposure of breccia he could find at the site, which he labelled 'Coopers A'. He also collected some fauna from the breccia dumps, all of which were prepared in the Transvaal Museum. This material formed part of a small collection that remained unstudied for several decades. However, since no hominins were recognized in the collection, Bob reported in his thesis, and later in his book, *The Hunters or the Hunted?*, that Coopers could not be considered a hominin site.

In 1994 Martin Pickford found a single hominin tooth in the boxes labelled 'Coopers' at the Transvaal Museum. In 1995 Lee Berger, Pickford and Francis Thackeray wrote a paper on the tooth describing it as probably belonging to a member of the genus *Homo*. Unfortunately, the fact that it had been found in the museum and not at the site left the question unresolved as to whether Coopers was indeed a hominin site. In 1999 Lee Berger decided to open a test excavation, starting at Coopers A, where about two to three square metres of breccia were exposed. He enlisted the help of a new graduate student, Christine Steininger, and instructed the team to make a small excavation into a decalcified solution cavity to collect a representative sample of fossils. At the same time, Steininger began sorting the collections of the Transvaal Museum to identify fauna for her Master's thesis. Shortly after beginning, she found the crushed face of a hominin in the boxes that had been overlooked for years. It would ultimately be assigned to the genus *Paranthropus*. This specimen was announced at the annual meeting of the American Association of Physical Anthropologists in 2000. Excavations did not continue in 1999 and there still remained the problem of no fossil hominin being found *in situ*. The possibility could therefore not be ruled out that this find had somehow come from another site and had mistakenly been put in the Coopers boxes at the Transvaal Museum.

Francis Thackeray and students at Kromdraai. (GG)

Lee Berger and Lazarus Kgasi discuss one of the latest finds at Coopers. (GG)

In May 2001 Berger resumed excavations at Coopers A, digging into the decalcified sediments and finding good fauna specimens. On the third week of excavation a group of field school students arrived from Duke University, and on a hunch Berger decided to have them dig on a small amount of exposed breccia about 60 metres from Coopers A. On the second day of work a deciduous hominin molar was found, probably belonging to a young *Paranthropus*. Over the next several months this area began to produce several fragments of hominins and wonderfully preserved faunal remains of pigs and sabre-tooth cats, as well as a host of other extinct fauna.

Coopers can be seen on guided tours arranged by one of the many registered tour operators found in the area. It also forms part of an interesting walk from Sterkfontein to Kromdraai.

Lucas Mothobi sieving fossils at Coopers. (GG)

BOLT'S FARM

Bolt's Farm is a series of discrete sites that may in fact have little or no association with each other, besides the fact that they fall within the boundaries of the old Bolt's Farm. You can see most of Bolt's Farm if you stand at Sterkfontein and look almost due west, to the left of Swartkrans. There you will see a large quarry, which was until recently an active lime-mining site, and a series of small farms and smallholdings.

There are numerous fossil-bearing sites in the area that can be identified by small outcroppings of trees. The area was a major focus of research by the United States-led Camp Peabody expedition of 1947. As yet, the only hominin find has been a single tooth, but unfortunately nobody knows exactly where it was found. There are currently three active digs on Bolt's Farm, one by the Transvaal Museum at a site that might be as old as 4 million years, and another two by the Palaeoanthropology Unit for Research and Exploration (PURE) of Wits, one of these in conjunction with the University of Pretoria. Many fantastic fossils have been recovered, including the nearly complete skeleton of a *Dinofelis* (extinct false sabre-tooth cat) species that may have fallen to its death while stalking trapped baboons.

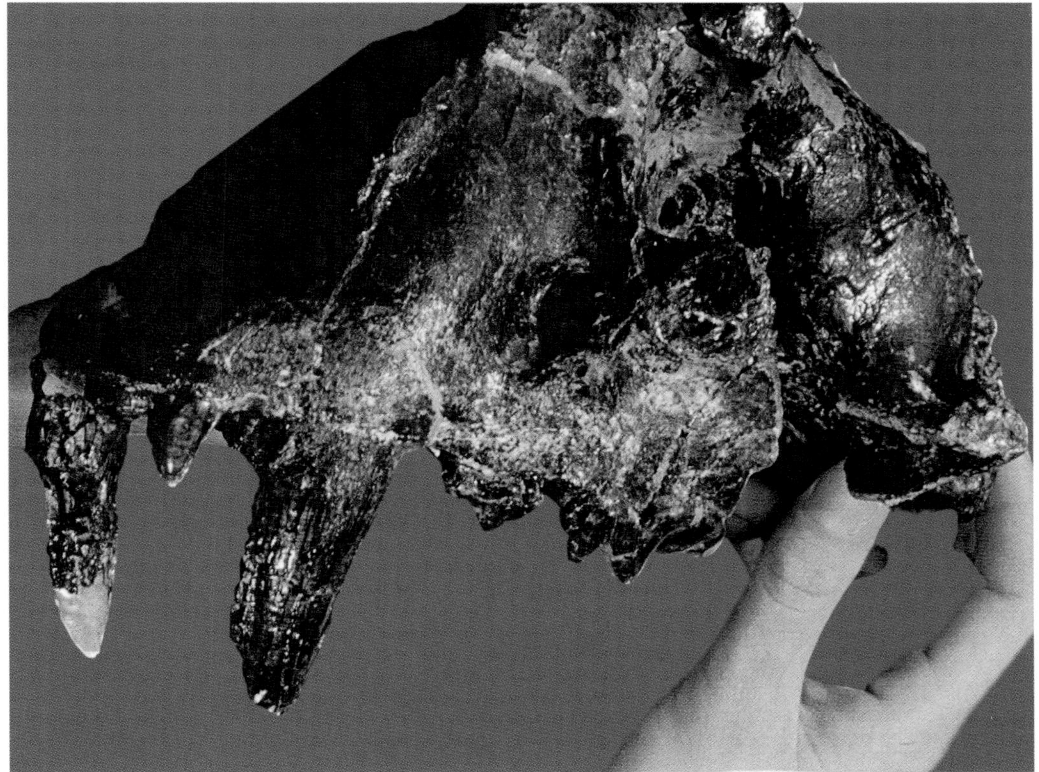

A **Dinofelis** *skull from Bolt's Farm.* (GG)

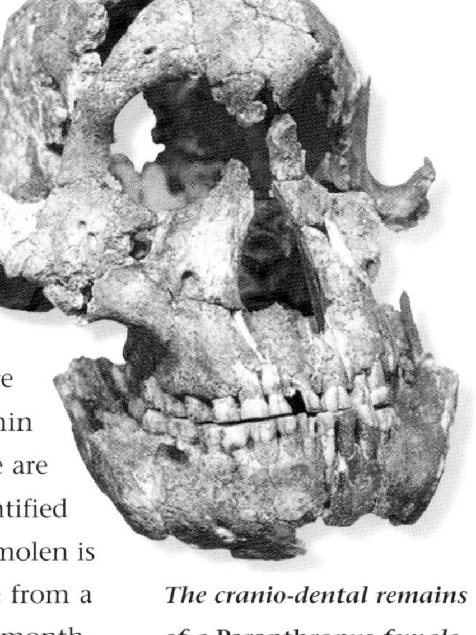

DRIMOLEN

Drimolen is a relatively new and as yet fairly unknown fossil site discovered in 1992. Excavation of the caves began shortly after it was discovered by Dr André Keyser of the Palaeoanthropology Unit for Research and Exploration at the University of the Witwatersrand. Like many of the other hominin sites, the caves were mined, in this case for calcite. So far 82 hominin specimens from Drimolen have been catalogued. These are mainly *Australopithecus robustus* and an as yet unidentified form of *Homo*. Most of the hominin material from Drimolen is cranio-dental. One of the *Homo* remains is a mandible from a child aged about 11, and the fossilized teeth of an eight-month-old robust australopithicine have also been found. The cave

The cranio-dental remains of a **Paranthropus** ***female found at Drimolen.*** (GG)

EXCAVATION TECHNIQUES

Excavation techniques have changed dramatically since the days when Robert Broom sifted through the rubble left by mine blasts to recover fossils. In the 1950s Bob Brain pioneered the use of then modern archaeological techniques at sites in the Cradle of Humankind, putting up permanent grid systems and piece-plotting fossils in the excavations at Swartkrans. More recently, even the faithful grid system, which had served palaeoanthropologists for almost four decades, has begun to vanish from sites in the Cradle, and now new sites use laser theodolites and GIS to plot fossil positions to sub-centimetre level.

Dorian Staps, a PhD student at PURE, using a laser theodolite. (GG)

infills from the main quarry, which is where most of the fossils have been extracted, are believed to be between 1,6 and 2,5 million years old. The kind of animal fossils found, including hyena, ancient baboons and a variety of extinct antelope, suggest that the climate at this time was similar to that of today, and that the environment consisted of rolling, grass-covered hills with patches of hill-slope forest and gallery forest along the water courses.

PLOVER'S LAKE

Plover's Lake is a fascinating series of sites with rich above-ground and underground fossil deposits dating back about 1 million years. The external deposits have been excavated to a limited extent by members of the Transvaal Museum. In early 2002, Lee Berger and a team from Duke University led by Steve Churchill began excavating the underground system of deposits, dating to between 60 000 and 120 000 years ago, where human remains have also been found. Visits can be arranged to the site and the ongoing dig through one of the recognized tour operators, or through PAST. Plover's Lake is also particularly suited to school tours, as it has an on-site museum and presents plays on the prehistory of the area.

NHS plaque at Plover's Lake. (GG)

A spring eye at Plover's Lake. (IJ)

WONDER CAVE

Wonder Cave is a large, open cavern reached by a lift that descends over 15 metres into a largely unmined stalactitic wonderland. It is one of the most accessible sites in the Cradle.

Inside this relatively 'young' cave, with limestone formations still growing, are a series of fossil deposits dating back many tens of thousands of years. Ask your guide to point out the many fossils of baboons that apparently fell from the narrow entrance and died there, preserved behind a flowstone curtain.

Inside Wonder Cave. (SIL)

GLADYSVALE

Gladysvale Cave is situated in the John Nash Nature Reserve, and like many other caves in the area was mined for limestone and guano. Mining occurred from 1902 to 1910 and then intermittently through the 1920s. Many fossils were found there during blasting operations before mining ceased altogether in 1928. Robert Broom visited the site in 1936 after a Mr G van Son reported seeing a human jaw in the breccia in the wall of the cave, but couldn't find it and assumed that vandals had removed it. Fossils collected by Broom include a small extinct monkey, a giant horse, the paratype of a large hyrax, as well as several other animals.

In 1945 Gladysvale was 'rediscovered' by a member of the newly formed South African Archaeological Society, Mr L Rosenberg, prompting subsequent visits by various luminaries in the fields of archaeology and palaeontology, such as Frank Peabody, as well as the young Phillip Tobias, who was one of Raymond Dart's students. A brief survey was conducted but no spectacular remains were reported. In 1946 Tobias led two brief student expeditions to the cave. A considerable amount of breccia was broken up and some fossil bones and teeth were collected, including that of a small baboon, *Papio izodi*, that was believed to have existed some 2,5 million years ago.

A fossil antelope jaw discovered at Gladysvale. (GG)

In 1948 Charles Camp and Frank Peabody of the University of California (UCLA) spent a month at Gladysvale blasting breccia and attempting to analyze the cave stratigraphy, finding many animal fossils but no hominins (their collection is still housed at Berkeley, California). For 40 years there was no further scientific activity at Gladysvale until a group led by André Keyser of the South African Geological Survey mapped out the subterranean chambers of Gladysvale. They found a few fossils, which piqued the interest of Dr Lee Berger. In October 1991, his work led to international renown for Gladysvale when it became the first new hominin-bearing site in South Africa in almost 40 years. Among the fossils was a pristine upper third premolar and an upper second molar. The third phase of excavation began in 1993 and has thus far recovered over 38 000 animal fossils from the Gladysvale rocks, including a large extinct, wolf-like animal.

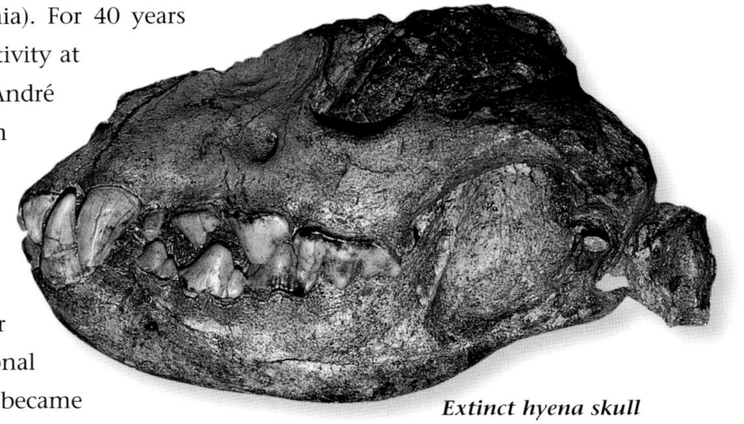

Extinct hyena skull from Kromdraai. (GG)

Gladysvale is extremely remote and in a pristine game reserve. Access can only be gained through a limited number of private tour operators, such as Hayward's Safaris (see Appendix), who have been granted permission by the landowner.

MOTSETSE

The 'newest' site in the Cradle, Motsetse site was discovered by Lee Berger in late 1999. It has been excavated intermittently since then, and has already produced wonderful fossils of primates and extinct false sabre-tooth cats. It is located near the Cradle restaurant and visitors to the site can enjoy a wonderful lunch overlooking a pristine Witwatersrand reserve. A game drive can be arranged at the restaurant or through a registered tour operator.

GONDOLIN

Gondolin is an old lime-works located near the northern edge of the Cradle of Humankind in near mountainous terrain. It was first noted as a fossiliferous deposit in 1977 by K MacKenzie, and sampling was soon undertaken by palaeontologist Elisabeth Vrba. Virginia Watson analyzed the fauna and suggested that the deposit was of similar age to Swartkrans,

***Kevin Kuykendall with the* Paranthropus *tooth from Gondolin.* (GG)**

namely 1,5–2 million years old. In 1997 excavations were re-opened by a team from the University of the Witwatersrand led by Kevin Kuykendall. André Keyser found the first hominin tooth shortly thereafter. This specimen has been tentatively assigned to *Homo*. Shortly after this discovery a PURE field technician, L Dihasu, discovered a second tooth that has been attributed to *Paranthropus*. Only limited sampling of Gondolin has occurred since. As the area is remote, tours of the site must be arranged through a recognized tour operator who has permission from the landowner.

HAASGAT

The Haasgat site is located in the northern aspect of the Cradle of Humankind and is not accessible to the public. It was excavated in the late 1980s and early 1990s by Dr André Keyser, then of the Geological Survey. Several dozen fine baboon specimens were found during the course of work at the site, but no hominins have been recovered to date. The site is thought to be approximately 1–1,5 million years old.

Mogale's Gate

Maropeng is Setswana for 'returning to the place of origin' and the Visitors' Centre here is shaped like an ancient burial mound known as a tumulus. It is located on the D400 a few kilometres off the main road to Sun City (R563) some six kilometres from Mogale City (Krugersdorp). A trip to Maropeng is an excellent way to begin one's exploration of the Cradle of Humankind as there is an extensive museum that tells the history of the world. It's a particularly good way to get children interested in human origins and natural history, as many of the displays in the 2 500 m^2 exhibition space are interactive and intriguing. There is an underground boat ride and a variety of displays. The site has a conference centre and a boutique hotel overlooking the wonderful Magaliesberg hills to the west. The ticket office here sells tickets for both the Visitors' Centre and the Sterkfontein caves. Guided tours are available. Maropeng is open seven days of the week between 09h00 and 17h00 and the last boat ride is at 16h00. For further information see **www.maropeng.co.za**

MINNAARS

The Minnaars cave site is a fossil-rich series of small caves located between Kromdraai and Plover's Lake. It has not been excavated yet but holds promise as a potential hominin-bearing site of early Pleistocene age. Several small carnivores have been recovered from the site by intermittent scientific visitors.

OTHER SITES IN THE COH

There are many other fossil-bearing cave sites throughout the Cradle of Humankind that are not accessible to the public or have not been opened for security reasons. However, there are a number of recognized tour operators who have access to the various sites. Their details are supplied in the information section at the back of the book. Please remember when visiting a site that it is illegal and unethical to remove any fossils or breccia from the Cradle of Humankind. Every tiny piece of the puzzle helps to reconstruct our heritage.

Main entrance to Wonder Cave. (IJ)

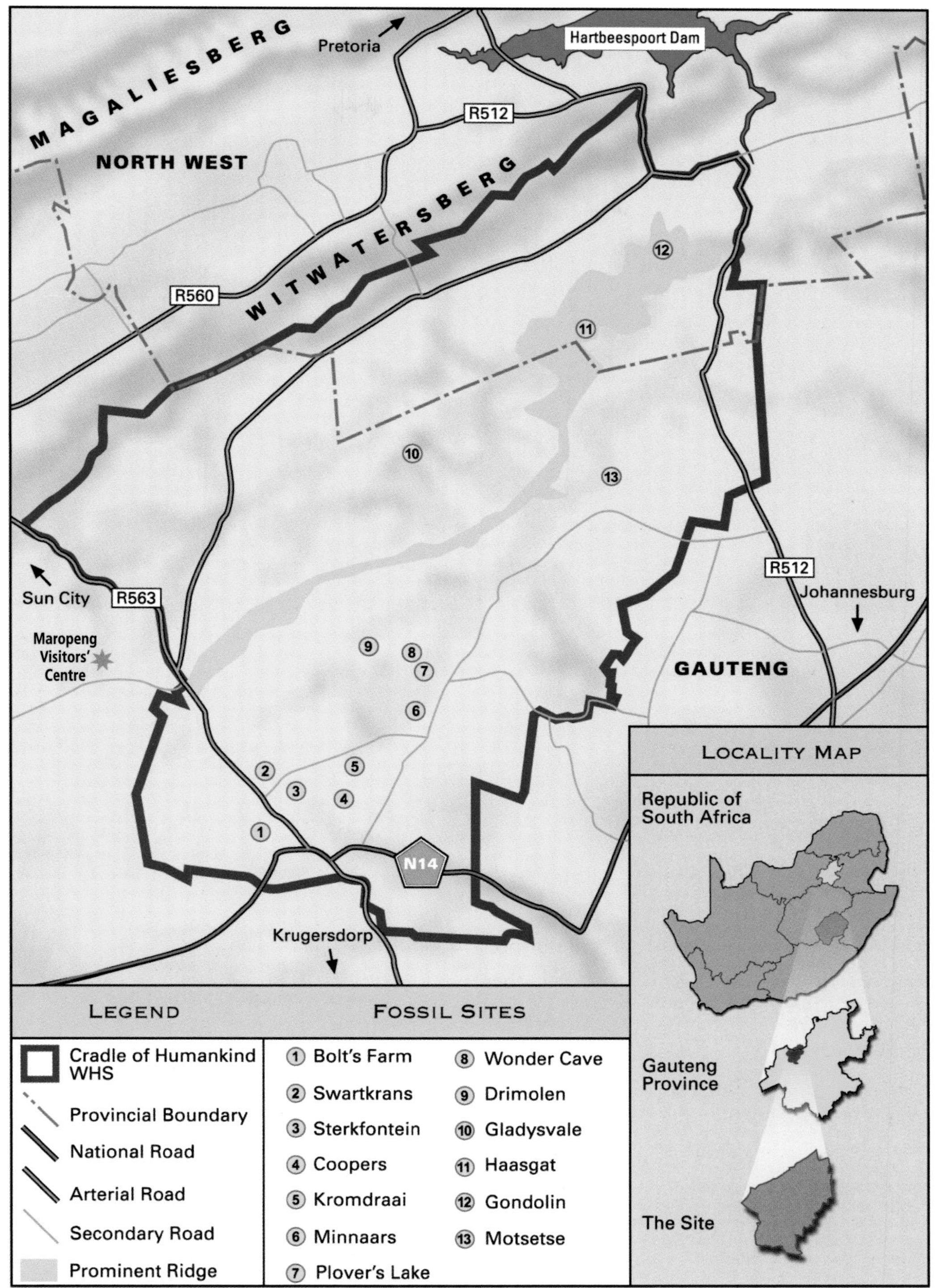
MAGALIESBERG
Pretoria
Hartbeespoort Dam
R512
NORTH WEST
WITWATERSBERG
R560
Sun City
R563
Maropeng Visitors' Centre
R512
Johannesburg
GAUTENG
N14
Krugersdorp
LOCALITY MAP
Republic of South Africa
Gauteng Province
The Site
LEGEND
Cradle of Humankind WHS
Provincial Boundary
National Road
Arterial Road
Secondary Road
Prominent Ridge
FOSSIL SITES
1 Bolt's Farm
2 Swartkrans
3 Sterkfontein
4 Coopers
5 Kromdraai
6 Minnaars
7 Plover's Lake
8 Wonder Cave
9 Drimolen
10 Gladysvale
11 Haasgat
12 Gondolin
13 Motsetse

PART THREE

FAUNA *and* FLORA

The declaration of the Cradle of Humankind as a World Heritage Site has precipitated a change in the land use of the area. Historically, its proximity to the urban centres of Johannesburg and Pretoria has meant that most of the development has been agricultural. The international recognition of its unique fossil heritage has conferred a new status upon the area, which is now governed by stringent guidelines set down by the United Nations Environmental, Scientific and Cultural Organization. As a result of this, environmental awareness of the animals and plants within the World Heritage Site has been heightened.

Although it does contain large tracts of unspoilt nature, the pristine wilderness areas of the Cradle of Humankind have been damaged by years of agricultural usage and by the introduction of non-native plants and animals. Environmental agencies are working to protect the original ecosystems that still exist in the Cradle of Humankind by removing artificially introduced species of plants and animals and rehabilitating damaged areas so that they may, at some time in the future, form part of a sustainable ecological system.

This fauna and flora section introduces the reader to some of the more common or spectacular extinct and extant plants and animals found in the Cradle of Humankind. It is important to note that while all of the extinct plants and animals found in the cave sites once lived in the area, not all of the living plants or animals now found in reserves in the Cradle of Humankind are historically native to the region.

ANIMALS

MAMMALS

This chapter lists creatures that currently roam the COH (Cradle of Humankind), as well as animals that now exist only as fossilized remains. This guide is intended as a general overview of the mammals, birds, reptiles, fish and insects of the area, as well as their evolutionary history.

An astute visitor to the COH will note that not all the animals are indigenous to the area. Many have been brought in by game managers. Animals such as the gemsbok, which did not occur here naturally in the past, are today found in great numbers, and do occur naturally only a few hundred kilometres north of the COH.

Other mammals, such as the springbok, pose more of a problem to ecologists, as historical records indicate that they did not occur in the region. However, the fossil record shows that they were abundant in the area throughout its history. Other animals, such as the elephant, should by rights still be found in the COH, but are not. Once abundant in the region, they were all shot out by the 20th century.

HOMININS

The COH has provided important evidence of the evolution of hominins for the last 2,5 million years. They are represented by members of the genus *Homo* as well as the genus *Australopithecus*. The genus *Australopithecus* can be traced as far back as 4,1 million years in Kenya. These earliest representatives of *Australopithecus* were already fully bipedal, though they were still characterized by small cranial capacities. *Australopithecus africanus* from Sterkfontein shows some of the same adaptations to bipedalism, and has been referred to by some as the direct, lineal ancestor to our own genus, *Homo*. Although very rare in the fossil assemblages of the COH, a number of specimens of *Homo* have also been found, providing significant insight into the evolution of our ancestors.

EXTINCT HUMAN ANCESTORS

Archaic humans – *Homo sapiens*

A great deal of scientific debate continues around the categorization of 'Archaic *Homo sapiens*' the forerunners of our own species, *H. sapiens sapiens*. Generally, the label applies to a variety of southern African fossil remains dated between 600 000 and 200 000 years ago, which is the bridging period between the existence of *H. erectus* and the appearance of modern humans. A handful of fossils, including the Florisbad skull from the

Free State, the Elandsfontein skull from the Cape West Coast and Kabwe Man (formerly known as the Broken Hill skull) from Zambia, have been classified as this transitional species, which appears to have slightly more primitive facial features compared to modern humans, including a more pronounced brow line. Archaic *H. sapiens* probably displayed the same capacity for complex social behaviour as early modern humans. It appears that there may be remains of archaic humans from Plover's Lake in the COH.

Homo erectus

Most scientists agree that *Homo erectus* is the youngest direct ancestor of *H. sapiens* (though some recognize an intermediary stage, *H. heidelbergensis*; if correct, this view would distance *H. erectus* by one stage in evolution, but not remove it from our family tree). *Homo erectus* was the first hominin species to move out of Africa, and its remains are therefore widespread throughout Africa, Europe, Asia and Indonesia. There is significant evidence that hunting and meat-eating were an important part of the everyday life of *H. erectus*. Almost certainly, *erectus* was able to communicate in some form of language. The species is known to have had a limited tool kit. They almost certainly had a wide habitat tolerance. Tantalizing evidence in Indonesia has raised the possibility that *H. erectus* was a capable woodworker, producing spears and perhaps even boats.

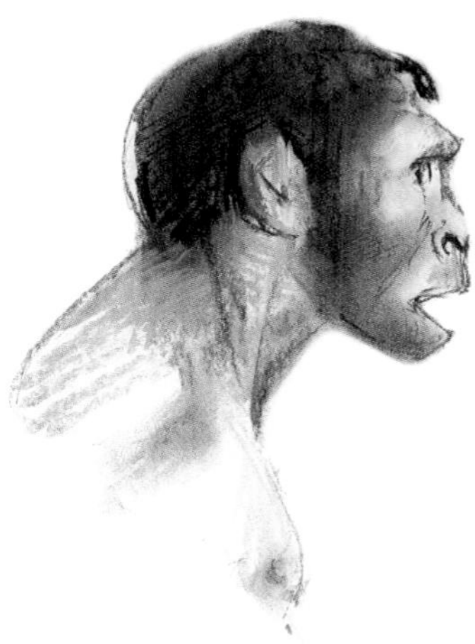

Homo erectus

Homo erectus remains have been recovered from Swartkrans Members 1 and 2, Drimolen, Coopers and possibly Gondolin, as well as numerous localities in East Africa. This species first appeared in Africa about 1,8 mya, and it probably vanished about 1 mya in South Africa, though it may have survived slightly longer than this estimate.

Homo habilis

Probably ancestral to *Homo erectus*, *H. habilis* was small in size, weighing approximately 40 kg. Little is known about this species, mainly because there is little agreement as to exactly which fossils can be ascribed to it, both in East and South Africa. It has been suggested that members of the species had the capacity for language, but this is difficult to confirm. It is possible that the earliest stone tools in Africa, found in Ethiopia and dated at 2,5 million years old, were produced by *H. habilis*, but there is too much controversy as to who the first tool makers were for this to be anything other than speculative.

Homo habilis

Homo habilis has been recorded exclusively in Member 5 of Sterkfontein, but

Australopithecus africanus

this identification is being questioned. It has also been found at Olduvai Gorge in Tanzania, as well as Koobi Fora in Kenya. It is estimated to have lived in Africa from about 2,5 mya until about 1,5 mya, when it became extinct.

***Australopithecus africanus* (gracile australopithecine)**
Australopithecus africanus may well be ancestral to the genus *Homo*, and thus potentially very significant to our evolutionary history. Their average body weight has been estimated at about 45,5 kg. Their arms were quite long relative to their legs, indicating a more chimpanzee-like body shape. This implies that they still spent some time in the trees, a conclusion supported by close observation of hand and foot bones.

Australopithecus africanus is endemic to South Africa, no remains having been found elsewhere at all. Their social organization might have been similar to that of chimpanzees. Diet probably consisted of fruits and leaves, though recent isotopic studies have suggested that a significant quantity of meat was also eaten. They would most likely have been scavengers rather than hunters. They probably occupied open environments such as woodlands, and may have included some form of grasses or sedges in their diet.

Australopithecus africanus has been found only in Sterkfontein Member 4 and possibly Gladysvale, although fossils of this species are also known from Makapansgat and Taung. The time range of *africanus* is somewhat restricted, probably due in large part to the limited number of sites containing fossils of the species, but it is thought that they existed between 3 and 2 mya.

***Paranthropus robustus* (robust australopithecine)**
The robust australopithecines are so called because of their more pronounced and powerfully developed facial muscles and bones. Although it was originally thought that this robusticity applied to the entire body, discoveries of bones have shown that they were not significantly larger than the gracile australopithecines, weighing about 47,7 kg. They were certainly more robust in the development of their skulls, which display massive attachments for powerful chewing muscles. They also had enormous teeth, and clearly did a significant amount of heavy chewing. Their diet most likely consisted of tough, fibrous vegetation such as roots, tubers and roughage. They may also have supplemented this vegetarian diet with termites, as tools found at Swartkrans appear to have been employed to break open the mounds of these insects. *Paranthropus robustus* is endemic to South Africa, and they probably had a wide habitat tolerance, as remains have been found in both open grassland and more closed woodland environments.

Australopithecus robustus

Remains of *P. robustus* have been discovered at Swartkrans Members 1–3, Kromdraai B, Drimolen, Coopers and Gondolin. They are not known anywhere outside the COH. The species existed from about 2 mya until approximately 1 mya.

NON-HOMININ PRIMATES

The non-hominin primates of the COH comprise several species of modern and extinct baboons and monkeys. Baboons first appeared in the late Miocene, probably 7–5 mya. There is a good fossil record of the various species. It is difficult to determine the precise evolutionary history of the baboons in southern Africa, but the oldest specimens of *Papio* (the genus of modern baboons) are to be found at Sterkfontein. Both the extinct and extant baboons of southern Africa are mostly omnivorous and terrestrial.

Cercopithecus monkeys are the most widespread and abundant monkeys in Africa. Their fossils, however, are extremely rare, and none have yet been found in South Africa. A single type of extinct leaf-eating monkey, *Cercopithecoides*, is known from the fossil caves of southern Africa, though leaf-eating monkeys are not found here today.

CHACMA BABOON
Papio cynocephalus ursinus

Chacma baboons tend to be dark brown, with an admixture of yellow or black hairs. They exhibit a large degree of sexual dimorphism, with males weighing approximately 32 kg, and females roughly 15 kg. Troop size is highly variable, and may number up to 150 individuals in optimal conditions. Several adult males may be present in larger groups, but the troop is always led by a dominant alpha male. Baboons are omnivorous, subsisting mainly on fruit and leaves, but they also include invertebrates, grasses, seeds, roots, flowers, bark, gums, mushrooms and occasionally reptiles, birds and mammals in their diet. Baboons are capable of adapting to a wide variety of habitats. They are restricted only by their need for suitable sleeping sites, such as caves or cliffs, that provide protection from predators.

Chacma baboon

Papio ursinus fossils are known from Member 5 of Swartkrans, and from Coopers.

HAMADRYAS BABOON
Papio hamadryas robinsoni

Originally accorded status as a separate species, *robinsoni* is now classified as a subspecies of the modern *hamadryas* baboon. Although the *hamadryas* baboon still exists today, it is no longer found in southern Africa, being restricted to the semi-desert Horn of Africa. In the past this was one of the most common baboons in the COH. Modern *hamadryas* baboons are smaller than chacma baboons, with males weighing about 19 kg, and females around 14 kg. The fossil *hamadryas* baboons were slightly larger than their modern counterparts.

Troops average about 100–150 individuals, but can grow as large as 350 animals. By day they forage for grasses, roots, flowers and fruits. The fossil form *Papio hamadryas robinsoni* almost certainly had a similar lifestyle to the modern *hamadryas* baboon.

Papio hamadryas robinsoni fossils are known from Swartkrans Members 1–3, Kromdraai A and B, Coopers, Bolt's Farm, Schurweburg, Gladysvale and Drimolen. This subspecies probably arose in South Africa some 2 mya, and disappeared sometime in the Pleistocene.

EXTINCT LARGE BABOON
Papio (Dinopithecus) ingens

The genus *Dinopithecus* was recently placed in the *Papio* genus because of the close similarities between the two types of baboon. This baboon is one of the biggest cercopithecoids known, being notably larger than modern baboons. Body size estimates place the largest specimens (presumably males) at greater than 40 kg. Significant sexual dimorphism is evident in the cheek teeth of this species. The shape of the skull and teeth is so similar to that of modern savanna baboons that we can presume they shared behaviour patterns. *Papio ingens* probably consumed a similar diet, including grasses, leaves, roots and fruits. The cheek pouches of this species were slightly different from those of modern baboons, suggesting there was some difference in feeding behaviour.

This species is known from the Hanging Remnant and the Lower Bank of Member 1 at Swartkrans, and from Coopers and Kromdraai A. As such, its known time span is somewhat limited to approximately 1,8–1,5 mya.

EXTINCT GELADA BABOON
Theropithecus oswaldi
This species of large, extinct baboon is closely related to the modern gelada baboon, found today in Ethiopia. *Theropithecus oswaldi* were much larger than their modern relatives, weighing in the neighbourhood of 40 kg. They probably had a diet similar to that of modern geladas, dedicated savanna grazers that subsist on a diet of grass and grass seeds. Their adaptation to terrestrialism is the most developed of all the non-hominin primates.

Extinct gelada baboon

The teeth of modern geladas and of *T. oswaldi* are high crowned to cope with excessive wear from eating grass. Their third molars erupt relatively late in life compared to other baboons so that when the earlier molars are wearing down, the third molars are just beginning to wear, prolonging the potential life span of the teeth in a fashion similar to elephants. Modern geladas have the most opposable thumb of all primates except humans. This provides them with a precision grip, as well as the ability to dig for rhizomes, roots and tubers during the dry season. The finger bones of *T. oswaldi* from Swartkrans appear similar to those of modern geladas. The social grouping of modern geladas is similar to that of *hamadryas* baboons, with smaller one-male harems and groups of bachelors banding together into groups of 50 to 250 individuals, although they sometimes number up to 600. It seems likely that the extinct form would have had a similar social organization.

Theropithecus oswaldi is known from Members 1–3 of Swartkrans and from Gladysvale and Coopers. Elsewhere in Africa fossils of *Theropithecus* dominate primate faunas from the late Pliocene until the mid to late Pleistocene, when they began to be replaced by savanna baboons (*Papio*).

EXTINCT SMALL BABOON
Parapapio jonesi
Of the Plio-Pleistocene baboons found in southern Africa, the genus *Parapapio* is the most primitive. There are actually four species assigned to this extinct genus, although there is some question as to the actual separation of the groups, since the main criterion for distinguishing the species is molar size. *Parapapio jonesi* is the smallest of the *Parapapio* species, with an estimated body weight of approximately 18 kg. *Parapapio jonesi* was probably a fruit and leaf eater, and its limb bones suggest it was arboreal. It was most likely adapted to forested environments.

Parapapio species are known from Sterkfontein Member 4, Swartkrans Member 1 and Kromdraai A. They range in time in South Africa from 3–1 mya. Several extinct species of *Parapapio* are known in East Africa, the oldest of which are more than 4 million years old. It is possible that *Parapapio* could represent the ancestral African baboon.

Vervet monkey

VERVET MONKEY
Cercopithecus aethiops
The vervet monkey of southern Africa is greyish in colour with a black face surrounded by a band of white hair. Males weigh about 5 kg, slightly more than the 4 kg females. They are common throughout the COH today, preferring to live in drier areas near permanent sources of water. However, they have a wide habitat tolerance, and will live in riverine woodlands if fruit is available. Vervets are diurnal and gregarious, living in small groups of up to 40 individuals, with several unrelated males co-existing. They are predominantly vegetarian, existing on a diet of fruits, flowers, leaves, seeds and seed pods, although they are known to eat insects as well as the occasional bird or bird egg.

The genus *Cercopithecus* is known from the late Pliocene, although surprisingly, given their widespread distribution in South Africa today, there are no known fossils of this genus in South Africa. The only fossils are from East Africa.

EXTINCT COLOBUS MONKEY
Cercopithecoides williamsi
The only true monkey found in the Sterkfontein Valley caves, this species is actually a colobine, or leaf-eating, monkey. They were much larger than vervet monkeys, weighing approximately 13 kg. Living colobine monkeys are arboreal, restricted to evergreen forest areas in equatorial Africa. The extinct monkey *Cercopithecoides* may have been able to live in less thickly wooded areas than are necessary for their closest living relatives, and were probably somewhat more terrestrial. The chewing muscles in *Cercopithecoides* were less powerfully developed than in modern colobines, but the teeth that have been found are often heavily worn. This suggests they were more likely to have eaten softer, grittier items, such as fruit and leaves, than modern colobines.

Cercopithecoides is known from the late Pliocene until the middle Pleistocene throughout Africa. Fossils have been recovered from Sterkfontein Member 4, the Lower Bank of Member 1 at Swartkrans, Member 2 at Swartkrans, Kromdraai B, Gladysvale and Drimolen. *Cercopithecoides* is also known from Makapansgat. It thus existed in South Africa from about 3 mya until just under 1,5 mya.

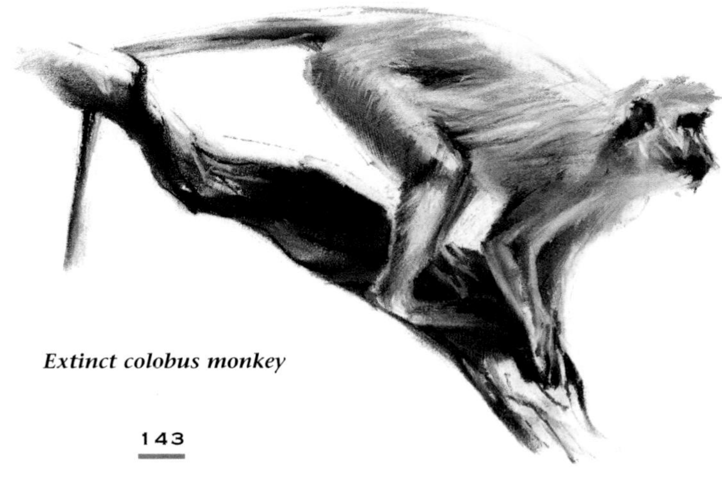

Extinct colobus monkey

Lesser bushbaby

LESSER BUSHBABY

Galago moholi

Lesser bushbabies are small and furry, with long tails, large eyes, and highly mobile ears. They are quite small, weighing on average 150 g, with little sexual dimorphism. Galagos have specialized ankle bones designed for quick running and leaping.

They are found in savanna woodlands throughout southern Africa, commonly associated with *Acacia* woodlands. They are abundant in the Mogale's Gate Reserve.

Lesser bushbabies are nocturnal and almost exclusively arboreal. During the day they rest in groups of two to seven, but forage separately. They may build themselves nests, or will occasionally occupy disused bird nests. Their diet consists exclusively of insects, and gums exuded principally by *Acacia* trees.

Galagos are known from as early as the Early Miocene in Africa, but have never been recognized in fossil form in South Africa.

LARGE FELIDS

The large cats found in the fossil caves of the COH can be divided into three main groups: the sabre-tooth cats, the false sabre-tooth cats, and the modern Pantherines (lion, leopard, cheetah). The sabre-tooth cats found in the COH belong to the subfamily Machairodontinae, and are typified by remarkably enlarged upper canines and reduced lower canines. These cats were the first successful large felid predators, overshadowing other carnivores from the Oligocene until their extinction in the Pliocene. The false sabre-tooth cats are characterized by the genus *Dinofelis*, the oldest representative of which is found at Langebaanweg on the Cape West Coast. The modern large felids of Africa first appeared about 3,5 mya in southern Africa.

LION

Panthera leo

The lion is the largest living terrestrial carnivore in Africa. Males are larger than females, the former weighing on average about 200 kg, and the latter around 125 kg. Lions once ranged across Africa, Europe and Asia, but today they are restricted to sub-Saharan Africa. Lions are mainly nocturnal, though they may also be active in daylight. They are distinctly social animals, operating collectively in prides ranging in size from a few individuals to as many as 30 lions. A single male usually dominates a pride of closely related females and their offspring. Occasionally there is more than one dominant male, but in this situation the males are usually closely related, most commonly

Lion

brothers. Lionesses do the majority of the hunting, with the dominant male appropriating kills before the females are allowed to feed. Lions take a wide variety of prey, from insects to buffalo. They have even been recorded taking a sub-adult bull elephant. Lions have a wide habitat tolerance, only avoiding forested areas. They do well in desert conditions, and can go for months without drinking, gaining moisture from the blood of their prey.

Lion fossils are known from Sterkfontein Members 4 and 5, Swartkrans Members 1–3, Kromdraai A, Coopers and Gladysvale. They first appeared roughly 3 mya, and were widespread across Africa during the Plio-Pleistocene.

Lions can be viewed in the COH at the Lion Park, the Rhino & Lion Nature Reserve and at Ngonyama Lion Lodge.

EXTINCT SABRE-TOOTH CATS

Homotherium crenatidens

Only distantly related to lions, these largest of the South African cats possessed the typically enlarged canine teeth that define sabre-tooth cats. The enlarged upper canines are serrated on both edges, and are almost delicately thin. The carnassial teeth are especially well adapted to slicing meat, but they would have had very little bone-cracking ability. The body size estimated for *Homotherium* is around 215 kg, which would have made them larger than modern male lions. These cats had powerfully built bodies, and would have been able to take down the largest of prey.

When hunting they most probably employed a stabbing technique, driving their large canines into the soft parts of their prey and then using a slicing motion to eviscerate them. It has been suggested that *Homotherium* may have hunted co-operatively in prides, perhaps as a mechanism to penetrate the protective shield walls adult Proboscideans form around their young when threatened. They were almost certainly the top predators until they became extinct. It is unlikely that *Homotherium* was a major threat to the hominins in the COH, since primates are particularly bony animals and any attack on such an animal would risk serious damage to their enlarged canines. Their large size, postcranial anatomy and presumed prey preferences indicate that these large cats would have preferred more open habitats as opposed to woodlands.

Homotherium is known only from Bolt's Farm and Kromdraai A in the COH, though it is also known from the grey breccia of Makapansgat, as well as E Quarry at Langebaanweg. It therefore existed from the Pliocene until the mid-Pleistocene (5–1,5 mya).

Megantereon cultridens

Similar to *Homotherium*, *Megantereon* also had the specialized upper canine teeth that mark the

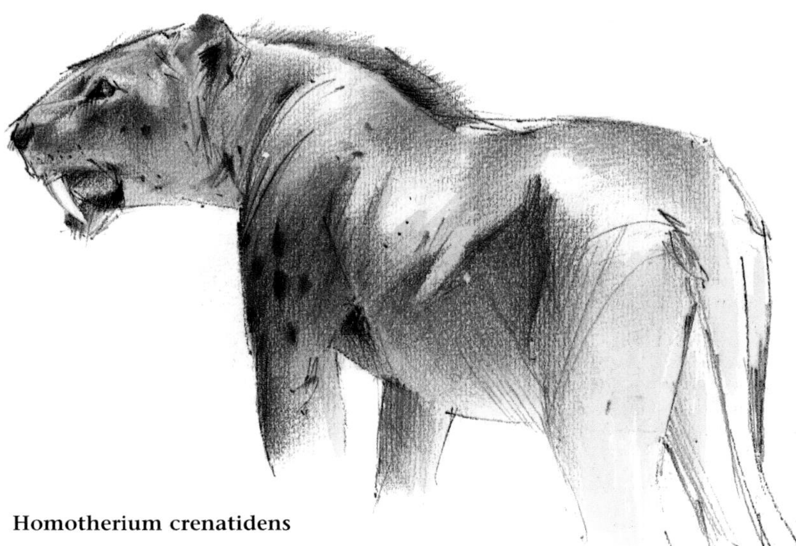

Homotherium crenatidens

Meganterеon cultridens

Machairodontinae. However, *Megantereon* did not have serrated sabre-teeth, though their canines were recurved, with very sharp edges. The carnassial teeth in *Megantereon* were also specifically adapted to the slicing of meat, and not the cracking of bone. It is possible that their stouter canine teeth would have been used to pierce the hides of thick-skinned ungulates, causing significant trauma and blood loss in their victims.

Megantereon were smaller sabre-tooth cats, weighing approximately the same as a large female lion (150 kg). They probably favoured more closed habitats, but would have been capable of taking larger prey than modern felids such as leopards and lions, although their skeletons were clearly not adapted for fast movement. It has been suggested that *Megantereon* dragged prey into trees much like leopards, but such behaviour would have posed a significant risk of damage to their canines from transporting heavy loads, and is therefore unlikely.

Megantereon is known from Sterkfontein Members 4 and 5, the Hanging Remnant of Swartkrans and perhaps Members 2 and 3, Kromdraai A and B and Coopers. The earliest appearance of this genus is at Langebaanweg at 5 mya, and it survived until just over 500 000 years ago.

LEOPARD

Panthera pardus

The modern leopard is arguably the most successful of the modern large cats, even in the face of human encroachment. The distinctive spots render them easily recognizable, though very difficult to spot when in grassy or wooded cover. Leopards are much smaller than lions, with males weighing on average 60 kg, and females 32 kg. Leopards have a very wide habitat tolerance, from deserts to forests, though they prefer areas with rocky outcroppings. Leopards are solitary and nocturnal, hunting primarily by stealth. In order to prevent theft of their kills, leopards will drag carcasses into trees for private consumption. However, if their range encompasses dolomitic caves, leopards prefer to drag carcasses into the depths of the caves for safety, which has had

Leopard

Dinofelis

significant impact on the bone accumulations in the fossil caves of the COH. Leopards are capable of subsisting on any form of animal protein, from insects to large bovids. They generally take prey not weighing more than 70 kg, though they have been documented killing animals as large as zebras and elands.

Leopards remain one of the most ubiquitous carnivores in the COH. Although elusive, they survive today in nature reserves and farmland, sometimes posing a threat to livestock. Their fossils have been found in Sterkfontein Members 2 and 4, possibly Member 5, Swartkrans Members 1–3, Kromdraai A and B, Gladysvale and Coopers. They first appeared just over 3 mya in South Africa, though they are known from sediments over 3,5 million years old in East Africa.

EXTINCT FALSE SABRE-TOOTH CAT
Dinofelis piveteaui

Dinofelis species lacked the elongated, curved canines of the Machairodontinae, and are therefore placed within the Felinae. This is why they are referred to as false sabre-tooth cats. Their canine teeth were somewhat elongated, though not as remarkably as in the sabre-tooth cats. They were also much stouter, similar to lions, but significantly larger. The estimated body size of *Dinofelis* was probably in the neighbourhood of 150 kg, similar to a large female lion. *Dinofelis* ranged from Europe, through East Africa and into South Africa. Their preferred habitat was probably a more closed environment, and their behaviour is hypothesized to have been rather similar to that of leopards. They are thus thought to have been solitary, nocturnal predators. Whether they preyed upon the hominins in the area is uncertain. Their larger body size and enhanced prey-grappling abilities would probably have allowed them to take larger prey than leopards quite regularly. *Dinofelis* would have had some tree-climbing ability, though its large size would have been a limiting factor. It has been suggested that *Dinofelis* may occasionally have scavenged carcasses dragged into trees by leopards. Their large size and powerful build would have made them one of the top predators in the Plio-Pleistocene.

Dinofelis are found in Sterkfontein Member 4, the Hanging Remnant and Member 2 of Swartkrans, Kromdraai A, Drimolen, Gladysvale, Motsetse and Bolt's Farm. They are also found in Langebaanweg, from about 5 mya, as well as in East Africa. By about 1 mya this genus had gone extinct.

Cheetah

CHEETAH

Acinonyx jubatus

Modern cheetahs are widely hailed as the fastest terrestrial animals in Africa. Their spotted coats and the distinctive 'tear-marks' under their eyes make them readily identifiable. Cheetahs are lightly built, with males averaging 54 kg and females 43 kg. They range all over modern Africa, though the encroachment of humans has significantly impacted on their distribution. Cheetahs live in open plains, but they are equally at home in savanna woodlands. These cats are primarily diurnal, and are dedicated terrestrial animals, running down their prey with short bursts of incredible speed. Cheetahs are at the bottom of the predator hierarchy, frequently losing their prey to hyenas, leopards and lions. To compensate for their timidity, they have evolved very efficient slicing teeth that enable them to rapidly eat as much of a carcass as possible before they are disturbed. Cheetahs are normally solitary, though they will band together to hunt larger prey such as young giraffe and water buck. Groups generally comprise closely related individuals, usually a mother and sub-adult or recently adult offspring.

Cheetah fossils are known only from Coopers and Swartkrans Members 2 and 3 at the COH. However, they can also be found at Makapansgat. They have existed for about 3 million years in South Africa, though they are older than 3,5 million years in East Africa.

They are bred today at the De Wildt Cheetah Centre, which supplies them to other game reserves and to zoos around the world. They also occur at Ngonyama Lion Lodge, the Rhino & Lion Nature Reserve, and the Lion Park.

Hyenas

During the Plio-Pleistocene, several types of hyena roamed the COH, about half of which became extinct. Hyenas may have developed their advanced bone-cracking abilities to process the carcasses that the sabre-tooth cats, with their exclusively meat-slicing teeth, left behind. Extinction in one part of a foodweb will affect other parts of the ecosystem, and it has been hypothesized that when the sabre-tooth cats went extinct, some of the hyenas followed suit, since the carcasses they depended on were no longer available. Some of the hyenas did survive, though. Although spotted hyenas used to be present in the COH, today only brown hyenas are found in the area.

SPOTTED HYENA

Crocuta crocuta

The peculiar spotted coat and sloping back of spotted hyenas make them readily identifiable. Their powerful neck and forequarters allow them to tear apart the largest of carcasses, dragging the heaviest remains with them. Females tend to be larger than males, averaging 69 kg and 62 kg respectively. Spotted hyenas are widely distributed in sub-Saharan Africa, though their range has shrunk as a result of human encroachment. They are a savanna species, preferring open plains or open woodlands; they avoid forested areas. Spotted hyena clans are matriarchal, with groups ranging from 4–18 or more adults occupying clearly delineated territories. They tend to be nocturnal, with extremely well-developed senses of smell, sight and hearing. They also have a highly developed repertoire of communication. Spotted hyenas are effective hunters, though they often lose prey to scavenging lions. Lions are the greatest threat to hyenas, as male lions will instinctively kill any hyenas they come in contact with. Spotted hyenas have a wide range of prey preferences, and can process bones from the largest of carcasses. They will crack a bone open, swallowing the fragments to extract nutritious content, then later regurgitate the remaining material.

Spotted hyena fossils are known from Sterkfontein Members 4 and 5, Swartkrans Members 1–3, Kromdraai A, Coopers and Gladysvale. In South Africa, Sterkfontein Member 4 and Makapansgat Member 4 have produced the oldest *Crocuta* remains at around 2,5 million years of age. This genus may have existed as far back as 4 mya in East Africa.

Extinct giant hyena

In the COH today, spotted hyenas occur only in the Rhino & Lion Nature Reserve.

Spotted hyena

EXTINCT GIANT HYENA
Pachycrocuta brevirostris

This extinct giant hyena was significantly larger than its closest living relative, the spotted hyena, weighing just under 100 kg. The genus was very widely distributed through Africa and Eurasia. Like spotted hyenas, they probably avoided forested and closed areas, preferring more open grasslands and woodlands. The large size and powerful build of *Pachycrocuta* would have enabled it to process the largest of carcasses, and access the contents of bones that other hyenas simply could not. It has been suggested that *Pachycrocuta* may have operated in clans similar to those of spotted hyenas, which would have made them formidable predators on the Plio-Pleistocene landscape. Their extinction has been linked to the demise of the sabre-tooth cats. Once these felid super-predators had vanished, the large carcasses they produced would no longer have been available for *Pachycrocuta* to scavenge. The giant hyena would then have had to compete directly with the smaller hyenas for smaller carcasses.

Pachycrocuta is known from Sterkfontein Members 4 and 5, Kromdraai A, Coopers and Gladysvale. It is also known from Makapansgat, extending its time range in South Africa from about 3 mya until about 1,5 mya. The genus survived in Eurasia until about 0,5 mya, and may thus have been present in Africa until that time.

BROWN HYENA
Hyena brunnea

Brown hyenas display the typical hyena build, with high shoulders and a sloping back towards the rump. Males are larger than females, with the males weighing roughly 47 kg and females weighing 42 kg. Brown hyenas are restricted to southern Africa, though in the past they were found throughout Africa. They tend to be found in arid areas such as deserts, but this may be a result of their being forced into more marginal areas, as they are known to prefer rocky areas with bush cover. Brown hyenas are nocturnal and extremely shy of humans, and thus are rarely seen. They are solitary foragers, though they live in groups in fixed territories and raise their young in communal dens. Group size can range from 5–14 individuals. Their senses are particularly well developed, and they can detect carcasses from several kilometres away. Brown hyenas are predominantly scavengers, though they will kill small mammals, birds, reptiles and insects. They will also eat ostrich eggs and wild tsama melons, the latter probably for their moisture content. Brown hyenas provision their young, taking portions of carcasses to their dens. As a result, hyenas are believed to have contributed to the accumulations of fossils in the COH.

Brown hyenas are known from Sterkfontein Members 4 and 5, Swartkrans Members 1–3 and Kromdraai A and B. They are also known from Makapansgat, which dates their existence in South Africa from 3 mya to the present.

They occur today in the wild throughout the COH.

EXTINCT HUNTING HYENA
Chasmaporthetes nitidula

Chasmaporthetes have been referred to as long-legged hunting hyenas. They were about the size of the brown hyena, with an estimated body weight of 40 kg. This genus was widely distributed through Africa and Eurasia. The long legs of these animals suggest they were more cursorial than modern hyenas, and may have engaged in more active hunting. Their

Brown hyena

Extinct hunting hyena

teeth do not show the same specialization for bone crushing as those of modern hyenas, and they were probably about as adept at this task as large felids. *Chasmaporthetes* may have been pack animals, and their meat-slicing tactics may have left significant scavengable carcasses in the palaeo-environment.

Chasmaporthetes are known from Sterkfontein Members 2, 4 and 5 as well as Swartkrans Members 1–3. They may also be derived from Member 2 of Sterkfontein, giving them a time range of over 3 mya until about just over 1 mya, when they vanished from southern Africa. In East Africa and Eurasia *Chasmaporthetes* existed over 4 mya.

AARDWOLF

Proteles cristatus

Aardwolves evolved from a hyaenid ancestor, and this ancestry is still visible in their high shoulders and sloping back. Males and females are approximately the same size, weighing about 9 kg each. They have a wide habitat tolerance, generally preferring open areas. Like hyenas, they tend to avoid forested areas. This is probably owing to the distribution of their main food source, harvester termites. These termites forage on the surface instead of underground, and are thus an easy source of food for the aardwolf. One species of termite the aardwolf feeds on is nocturnal, and thus so is the aardwolf. However, South African winters are often too cold for the termites to forage, so the aardwolf switches to another species of termite that is diurnal. They are entirely solitary unless accompanied by their offspring. Aardwolves are so adapted to their termite diet that their teeth have become reduced to the extent that they can no longer feed on any other form of animal protein.

Fossil representatives of aardwolves are known from Sterkfontein Member 5, Swartkrans Members 1–3 and Kromdraai B. As a result, their time range in the COH is restricted from about 1,5 mya until the present. Fossil aardwolves are unknown in East Africa.

CANIDS

The fossil canids of the COH are only poorly understood, having been eclipsed by the more spectacular felids and hyaenids. It is becoming apparent that many more types of canid were present in the fossil caves than have been recognized to date. Canids in general are remarkable for having remained generalized feeders, capable of consuming both animal and

Black-backed jackal

plant matter. Canids have preserved most of their dentition, as opposed to hyenas and cats, which lost most of their molar teeth as they evolved over time. As a result, canids tend to have elongated snouts that also endow them with a very well-developed sense of smell. Foxes and bat-eared foxes are represented in the assemblages from Sterkfontein, Swartkrans and Kromdraai, though they are extremely rare. The genus *Nyctereutes*, the racoon-dog of Asia, has also been recognized at Kromdraai, the first record of this animal in Africa.

BLACK-BACKED JACKAL
Canis mesomelas

Black-backed jackals are distinguished from other jackals by the broad, dark saddle that covers their back from the neck to the tail. Males weigh about 8 kg, and females about 7 kg, their small size making them subordinate to felids and hyaenids in confrontations over carcasses. They have a wide habitat tolerance, occurring in savanna and arid zones, but preferring drier areas. Jackals exhibit both diurnal and nocturnal activity patterns in response to the activities of their principal prey, rodents. The distinctive call of the jackal is one of the definitive sounds of the African bush. Jackals subsist on insects, rodents, reptiles and birds. They also scavenge whenever possible, putting significant pressure on hyenas in competition for carcasses. Jackals do not hunt animals larger than springhares, but will occasionally kill the young of small bovids.

Jackals are well represented in the fossil caves of the COH, but the taxonomy of these small carnivores is not well understood. The genus *Canis* is known from Sterkfontein Members 4 and 5, Swartkrans Members 1–3, Kromdraai A and B, Gladysvale, Drimolen and Coopers. *Canis* is also known from Makapansgat, which means that its range extends from 3 mya to the present.

They are found in the wild throughout the COH today.

WILD DOG
Lycaon pictus

The blotched black, white and yellow coat of the wild dog, along with its large round ears, make this animal unmistakable. Wild dogs weigh about 30 kg in South Africa, with males slightly larger than females. They used to be widespread throughout Africa, but there has been a remarkable reduction in their distribution and population size. They are bred at the De Wildt Cheetah

Wild dog

Centre in the COH, which supplies them to other game reserves and exports them to zoos. Wild dogs prefer open plains or open savanna woodlands, and since they hunt mainly by sight, they avoid forested areas, woodlands and grasslands with tall grass cover. They are diurnal, and have evolved the specialized pack behaviour of dogs to procure food. Packs range in size from 3–28 individuals on average, though some packs numbering more than 40 have been recorded. The young are well cared for by all members of the pack, and all the animals in a group are highly interdependent. Wild dogs hunt by coursing after their prey: they start chasing an animal, and relentlessly follow it at moderate to high speed until the animal falls from exhaustion or trauma inflicted by the dogs. This technique is particularly effective, and large packs are very successful. Once an animal has been caught it is completely consumed within a short period of time. Wild dogs will defend kills from hyenas, often causing severe injury to the hyenas through their mobbing behaviour.

Claims for the presence of wild dogs in the fossil sites of the COH have been received with scepticism. The oldest confirmed record to date of *Lycaon pictus* in South Africa is from Elandsfontein at about 0,5 mya. *Lycaon pictus* is known from East Africa about 2 mya.

Extinct wolf-like dog

EXTINCT WOLF-LIKE DOG
Lycaon esabagyus

This recently discovered species of wild dog may represent the oldest evidence for wild dogs in South Africa. It is a large animal, approximately the size of a modern North American wolf. It probably had an omnivorous diet, as a seed from a wild date palm was found in its abdominal cavity. So far it has only been recovered from Gladysvale, and is estimated to be just under 1 million years old.

Caracal

SMALLER CARNIVORES

Numerous small carnivores inhabit South Africa, and many have been found in the fossil caves of the COH. For the most part, fossil finds are very rare. These smaller animals probably did not play a significant role in the accumulation of bones in the fossil caves. Rather, they were most likely brought into the caves by animals such as leopards and brown hyenas.

CARACAL

Felis caracal

Caracals are reddish brown in colour with conspicuous tufts of hair at the tips of their ears. Males average about 14 kg in weight, while females reach about 12 kg. Caracals inhabit arid open country and savanna woodlands where cover is minimal. They have a varied diet, that includes small bovids, hyraxes, rodents and other small carnivores. They occasionally take birds and even fish. Caracals are solitary and predominantly nocturnal, even in undisturbed areas. Although mainly terrestrial, like most cats caracals are adept tree climbers. Caracals are difficult to spot, particularly at night.

Caracal fossils are known from Kromdraai A, the Lower Bank of Swartkrans and from Drimolen. They are also known from Makapansgat. Their fossil record thus extends from 3 mya to the present in South Africa. They can be traced back to about the same time in East Africa.

MEERKAT

Suricata suricatta

Meerkats tend to be silvery brown, with a long tail and stocky hindquarters. Both males and females weigh around 750 g, though the males are usually slightly larger than the females. They are restricted to southern Africa, being well adapted to open, arid regions with hard or stony substrates. Meerkats are diurnal, operating in tightly knit social groupings of 2–30 members. Their characteristic habit of sitting on their haunches to survey their immediate environment is a classic pose among African wildlife. They are extremely wary and always on the alert against eagles and jackals. Their diet consists in large part of insects, as well as reptiles, amphibians and birds.

Meerkat

Meerkat fossils are known from the Hanging Remnant of Swartkrans, Members 2 and 3 of Swartkrans, Coopers and possibly from Drimolen. Their time range in South Africa therefore extends from about 1,5 mya to the present.

PROBOSCIDEANS AND HYRACOIDS

The Proboscidea are animals with a mobile proboscis, or nose, such as elephants and their extinct ancestors. In what appears to be an absurd twist of nature, the closest living relatives of elephants are the tiny hyraxes, or dassies, survivors of an ancient group of near-ungulates that links the elephant and hyrax together with aardvarks and dugongs! Once a specious group known as the Paenungulata, the rise of the true ungulates whittled their numbers down to the few forms living today.

Elephants have played an important role in the study of the evolution of mammals in East Africa. The depositional

Elephant

environments in East Africa often preserve elephant skulls intact. In South Africa, the collecting agents that accumulate bones in the fossil caves rarely brought elephants into their lairs, and as such less is known about the evolution of these large animals here. For the most part, elephant remains consist of tooth fragments derived from juveniles. Hyraxes, on the other hand, are abundant and better known in South Africa than in East Africa.

ELEPHANT

Loxodonta africana

The largest of all modern terrestrial mammals, the tusked and trunked elephants are readily identified. Bull elephants weigh on average 5 000 kg, and cows 3 000 kg. Elephants have a wide habitat tolerance, living everywhere from deserts to lush woodlands, their main requirement being a water source. Elephants are social animals, living in groups of two to several dozen individuals. Groups are composed of several related females and their offspring, led by a dominant matriarch. At puberty males leave the herd of their own accord, rejoining female herds only when one of the females is in oestrus. Elephants are both diurnal and nocturnal, ranging long distances in search of food. They are known to both browse and graze, eating a variety of different plants. Although their eyesight is poor, elephants have a very good sense of smell and well-developed hearing.

Fossils of the genus *Loxodonta* are known only from Bolt's Farm in the COH. In East Africa *L. africana* can be traced back to just over 1,5 mya.

The only place to view elephants in the COH is at the Elephant Sanctuary, where they can be experienced at close quarters.

EXTINCT ELEPHANT

Elephas recki

The extinct elephant was slightly smaller than modern elephants. It differed from modern elephants in having smaller tusks and reduced premaxillae, the bones in which

Extinct elephant

the tusks grow. The face of *Elephas recki* was more compressed, and the back of the skull was larger compared to *Loxodonta*. *Elephas recki* is known from East and South Africa. This species of elephant probably had a diet similar to that of modern elephants, consisting of both browse and graze. Virtually all the remains in the COH fossil sites are of juveniles.

Elephas recki is known from Sterkfontein Member 4, Swartkrans Members 1 and 3, and Gladysvale. It is probable that it existed at Makapansgat as well, giving it a time range of 3–1 mya in South Africa. It had a similar time span in East Africa.

ROCK HYRAX
Procavia capensis

Rock hyraxes are small compact animals lacking tails. They have a curved claw on the second digit for grooming. Males weigh about 4,5 kg, and females are slightly smaller. Rock hyraxes live in rocky krantzes and outcrops with associated bushes and trees to provide browse, and nooks and crannies where they can hide in case of danger. Their main predators are eagles and leopard. Hyraxes are mainly diurnal, living in social groups that can number in the hundreds and are divided into a series of harems. They have padded, permanently moist feet that provide them with a firm footing on the rocks. They eat a variety of grasses, forbs and shrubs, some of which are poisonous to other mammals.

Rock hyrax

Extinct giant hyrax

Procavia capensis is a recent species that appears only in Member 5 of Swartkrans, dated to approximately 11 000 years ago.

Hyraxes are widespread throughout the COH.

EXTINCT GIANT HYRAX
Procavia transvaalensis

This species of extinct hyrax was about one-and-a-half times the size of modern rock hyraxes, weighing an estimated 6,5–7 kg. Other than the size difference, *Procavia transvaalensis* was very similar to modern hyraxes. It can therefore be presumed that it had a similar diet and lifestyle. The species was originally named for a large hyrax recovered from Coopers in 1936. Many of the crania known from sites such as Swartkrans show evidence suggesting that it was eaten by leopards and eagles, much the same as today.

Procavia transvaalensis is known from Sterkfontein Members 4 and 5, Swartkrans Members 1–3, Kromdraai A and probably B, Gladysvale, Coopers, Motsetse and Bolt's Farm. It is also known from Makapansgat, which suggests that it occurred in South Africa from 3 mya until its disappearance sometime in the Pleistocene.

EQUIDS

Horses have a long evolutionary history, extending back as far as the Miocene in Africa. The equids can be divided into two basic groups in southern African fossil sites: the three-toed *Hipparion* and the single-toed *Equus*. *Hipparion* is the more primitive form, first appearing in the Miocene and surviving until the end of the Pleistocene, at which point it went extinct. The more advanced *Equus* first appeared in the Pliocene of North Africa, and soon after that in southern Africa. The genus *Equus* is of special importance for dating the fossil localities in

Africa, since the genus first appeared about 2,4 mya in Africa. Therefore, any fossil locality containing *Equus* cannot be older than 2,4 million years. Equids are rare fossils in the COH.

ZEBRA
Equus burchellii

The characteristic striping of zebras renders them readily identifiable, as well as providing camouflage in tall grasses. Burchell's zebra males weigh on average 313 kg, while females tip the scales at approximately 302 kg. They are restricted in distribution to the area extending from the northern part of southern Africa into East Africa. Burchell's zebras are adapted to open savanna plains, preferring open areas of woodland, scrubland and grassland as long as water is available. The bulk of their diet comprises grasses, though they have been known to browse on occasion. They are capable of subsisting on all parts of the grasses, including leaves, sheaths and stems. Zebras live in social groups of three to several dozen individuals, led by a dominant stallion and one or more of the mares and their foals.

Zebra

Equus burchellii fossils are known from Sterkfontein Members 4 and 5, Swartkrans Members 1–3, Kromdraai A, Gladysvale and Coopers. The oldest record of *Equus* in South Africa comes from Sterkfontein Member 4.

Zebras can be seen in most of the nature reserves in the COH.

EXTINCT CAPE HORSE
Equus capensis

Equus capensis, the giant Cape horse, was first described by Broom in 1909 based on fossils recovered near Cape Town. This horse was significantly larger than modern zebras, weighing an estimated 895 kg. Its skeleton was differently proportioned to that of modern zebras, as it had a more powerfully built, but shorter, body, and a more massive head. *Equus capensis* had a wide distribution, having been recovered from sites across southern and East Africa. Its social organization was probably very similar to that of modern zebras. Diet can be reconstructed to have been predominantly graze, as is the case with all members of the genus *Equus*.

Extinct Cape horse

Equus capensis has been recovered from Sterkfontein Member 4, Swartkrans Members 1–3, Kromdraai A, Gladysvale and Coopers. It made its last appearance at Equus Cave near Taung, in early Holocene times.

EXTINCT THREE-TOED HORSE
Hipparion lybicum

The three-toed *Hipparion* is the most primitive horse in the COH. The three toes on each foot were fully functional, whereas in *Equus* only the third toe bears weight, with the other toes reduced in size to useless 'splint' bones. *Hipparion* is estimated to have been larger than modern zebras, weighing approximately 489 kg. Its remains can be found throughout East

Africa, indicating it was widely distributed in Africa. *Hipparion* was most likely a grassland grazer and quite water dependent.

Hipparion lybicum can be found in Swartkrans Members 1–3, Kromdraai A and possibly at Gladysvale.

VERY LARGE MAMMALS

The two types of modern rhinoceros in Africa have different evolutionary histories. The ancestors of the white rhino first appeared in Kenya just over 7 mya. The ancestors of the black rhino first appeared in Europe, Asia and North Africa nearly 12 mya, while the modern species first appeared about 4 mya at Kanam West in East Africa. Conspicuous by its absence, no rhinoceros fossil has yet been identified in the COH, although live white rhinos can be viewed at the Rhino & Lion Nature Reserve.

Hippopotami, however, are known in the COH. The earliest hippopotamus occurred in the Miocene in Kenya about 7 mya. The direct ancestor of the modern hippopotamus first appeared in the early Pleistocene of Uganda, and modern hippos had evolved by the mid-Pleistocene.

WHITE RHINO

Ceratotherium simum

White rhino are best characterized by their square lips. The designation 'white' comes from the Dutch word 'witte', meaning wide, a reference to the lips of this animal, and thus mistranslated as 'white' into English. In reality, white rhinos are grey, much like black rhinos. Male white rhinos weigh between 2 000 and 2 300 kg, while females are smaller at 1 600 kg. The characteristic horns of the rhino have long been prized by hunters. Although their range was significantly larger in the past, white rhinos are now very limited in distribution, concentrated in South Africa. White rhinos require flat grasslands with adequate bush cover and standing water for drinking and wallowing. They are found in small groups comprising a dominant, territorial bull, subordinate bulls, cows and their offspring. White rhinos are mostly grazers, preferring short grasses that they crop with their sensitive upper lip (they have no incisor teeth). They are active mainly in the daytime, and although their eyesight is poor, they have excellent senses of smell and hearing. They do not react as aggressively as black rhinos towards intruders.

No white rhino fossils have been recovered in the COH, though they are known from Makapansgat, which gives them a time range from 3 mya until the present in South Africa. It is interesting to note that isotopic studies of *Ceratotherium simum* from

White rhino

Hippopotamus

Makapansgat indicate that they included much more browse in their diet than do their modern counterparts, suggesting that in Makapansgat times they had not yet adapted to a 100 per cent grass diet.

HIPPOPOTAMUS

Hippopotamus amphibius

Hippos have large, barrel-shaped bodies with short, stout legs. Male hippos average about 1 500 kg, while females are somewhat smaller at 1 300 kg. The basic habitat requirement of hippos is a body of standing water in which they can submerge themselves completely. They are primarily nocturnal, ranging over long distances on dry land in search of food. During the day they rest in their pools or bask in the sun. During the day, hippos congregate in groups of varying size and composition, generally consisting of females with calves and associated bachelors. They will graze solitarily or in mother-offspring groups. Hippos are selective grazers, preferring open areas of short, green grass. Hippos are among the most dangerous animals in Africa, accounting for more human fatalities than all the carnivores combined.

Hippopotamus is known from Swartkrans Members 1–3, as well as Makapansgat, and has thus been found in South Africa from 3 mya until the present.

SUIDS

The evolution of suids in Africa has been studied intensively for several decades. As a group, suids tend to evolve at a rapid rate, and thus are very important for biostratigraphic comparisons between the well-dated East African fossil deposits and the less securely dated South African ones. It is therefore unfortunate that suids are exceedingly rare in the fossil assemblages of the COH. The only exception is the newly opened site of Coopers, which has already produced a wealth of fossil suids. The oldest ancestors of the Suidae existed during the Oligocene, though the ancestry of the suids found in South Africa is much more recent. *Phacochoerus*, the genus of the modern warthog, can be traced back to near the beginning of the Pleistocene, approximately 1,8 mya. The other 'common' fossil suid in South Africa, *Metridiochoerus*, also has its origins at around this time.

WARTHOG

Phacochoerus aethiopicus

Warthog males average about 100 kg in weight, while females are more petite at 70 kg. They are typically associated with open grasslands, floodplains, vleis and open areas around waterholes. They will also occupy open scrublands and woodlands. Warthogs prefer to graze on short, fresh grasses, but will also eat sedges, herbs, shrubs and wild fruit. While rooting for food, warthogs kneel on their front legs and use their snouts to dig in the ground. Warthogs are diurnal, hiding out in burrows during the day to protect themselves from predators and inclement weather. They are social animals, living in family units called sounders, which comprise an adult male, adult female and her offspring. The group usually numbers five or less.

Phacochoerus fossils are known in Members 1–3 of Swartkrans, Kromdraai A and B, Gladysvale and possibly Coopers. Warthogs are therefore known in South Africa from about 1,8 mya until the present.

They can be found in most of the nature reserves in the COH.

Extinct pig

EXTINCT PIG

Metridiochoerus andrewsi

Metridiochoerus resembled warthogs, except that their tusks were essentially straight, projecting laterally from the sides of the muzzle. They were larger than warthogs, probably weighing in excess of 120 kg. They were most likely grazers, probably living in the open, watered areas also preferred by warthogs.

Metridiochoerus is known from Swartkrans Members 1–3, Kromdraai A, Coopers and Bolt's Farm in the COH. It is also known from Makapansgat around 3 mya, as well as Elandsfontein at 0,5 mya.

GIRAFFES

The earliest giraffes in Africa are found from the Miocene in Libya. The entire giraffe lineage probably originated in Africa, and then spread into Eurasia. All non-African lineages of giraffe subsequently went extinct, leaving two types surviving in Africa, the giraffes and the okapis. The first member of the genus *Giraffa* appeared in the late Miocene, while the modern giraffe (*Giraffa camelopardalis*) appeared in the early Pleistocene in East and South Africa. The extinct short-necked giraffe *Sivatherium* first appeared in the early Pliocene, but is distinctly separate from its long-necked cousins.

Warthog

GIRAFFE

Giraffa camelopardalis

The long neck of the giraffe, along with its enormous size, make this animal one of the most enduring images of Africa. Bull giraffes weigh on average 1 200 kg, while females are lighter at about 830 kg. They can live in a variety of habitats, ranging from dry savanna to woodlands, provided their preferred food plants are present. Giraffes predominantly browse, including a variety of food plants in their diet. They are mainly diurnal, though they do occasionally move around at night. Giraffes are only loosely social, and herds tend to be made up of females and their young, though bachelor herds and mixed herds are sometimes encountered.

Giraffe

Giraffes are found in most reserves in the COH.

Fossils of modern long-necked giraffes are known only from Gladysvale in the COH, though their immediate predecessor, *Giraffa jumae*, is known from Makapansgat at around 3 mya.

EXTINCT SHORT-NECKED GIRAFFE

Sivatherium maurusium

The short-necked giraffe *Sivatherium* is the largest and most massive giraffe that ever existed in Africa, weighing up to 2 000 kg. *Sivatherium* probably lived in similar habitats to modern giraffes, ranging from savannas to woodlands. Isotopic studies of their fossils show that this giraffe was a dedicated browser, and may have been more dependent on water than modern giraffes. It may also have fed at a lower level than modern giraffes.

Sivatherium maurusium was initially known in the COH from a single deciduous tooth in Member 2 of Swartkrans, though recent examination of faunal collections has revealed giraffid postcranial remains in all members of Swartkrans. It has also recently been found at Coopers. Elsewhere in South Africa, this species is known from Makapansgat and Langebaanweg, as well as the Pleistocene sites of Florisbad, Cornelia and Elandsfontein. This species was thus present in South Africa from approximately 5 mya until as recently as 0,4 mya.

Extinct short-necked giraffe

BOVIDS

Bovids are typically the most abundant type of animal in the fossil sites of the COH, often dominating the assemblages. Their ability to adapt to open country and very arid regions is at least partly responsible for their remarkable success. Bovids are easily distinguished from cervids (the deer of North America and Europe) because they possess keratin-sheathed horns as opposed to seasonally shed antlers. These horns are always diagnostic criteria by which living and fossil bovids can be identified. The earliest bovids in Africa probably originated in the Oligocene, but it is difficult to separate them from their ancestral forebears. By the time of Langebaanweg in the Western Cape (5 mya), many of the species recognizable today had emerged. Bovids are particularly important when studying the caves in the COH. They are useful for biostratigraphic comparisons when assessing the age of fossil caves, and provide a great deal of insight into the palaeoenvironment in which hominins lived. They can also shed light on the taphonomic history of the deposits, answering questions on how the fossils came to end up in the caves, and what types of carnivores may have fed on them. Most of the bovid species found in the fossil caves still exist today, though a number have gone extinct in the past 2,5 million years.

BLUE WILDEBEEST

Connochaetes taurinus

Blue wildebeest have humped shoulders and a deep neck, sloping towards more lightly built hindquarters. Males average about 250 kg, while females are closer to 180 kg. Blue wildebeest are associated with arid environments, including savanna woodlands and open woodlands. Their main requirements are shade and drinking water. Blue wildebeest are grazers, preferring short green grasses, in particular fresh sprouting grass. They are gregarious and occur in herds numbering from 20 or 30 individuals to many thousands. Social groupings consist of territorial males, female herds and bachelor groups.

Blue wildebeest

Blue wildebeest were quite ubiquitous in the COH, as their fossils have been found in Sterkfontein Members 4 and 5, Swartkrans Members 1–3, Kromdraai A and B, Gladysvale, Drimolen, Coopers, Bolt's Farm and Motsetse. Fossils of blue wildebeest are also commonly found throughout East Africa. Elsewhere in South Africa their fossils are common at sites such as Elandsfontein, Cornelia and Florisbad. The species appears to range from about 2,5 mya until the present.

Blue wildebeest are found on most private game reserves in the COH.

BLACK WILDEBEEST

Connochaetes gnou

Black wildebeest are smaller than blue wildebeest, with a long white tail almost reaching the ground, as opposed to the shorter black tail of blue wildebeest. Males weigh approximately 160 kg, while females average around 130 kg. Black wildebeest are endemic to South Africa, and are not found further north than the 27th parallel. They are adapted to open plains and grasslands. During the winter months they will also supplement their diet with browse from karroid bushes. Like blue wildebeest, black wildebeest are gregarious, with a social organization consisting of territorial males, female herds and bachelor groups. They do not migrate.

Black wildebeest

Black wildebeest evolved only recently, and are therefore not found as fossils in the COH. Fossils have been recovered from South African sites such as Elandsfontein, Cornelia and Florisbad. The species probably evolved about 500 000 years ago, surviving until the present.

Black wildebeest are found only in a few private reserves in the COH, such as the John Nash Nature Reserve.

RED HARTEBEEST
Alcelaphus buselaphus

Red hartebeest have high, humped shoulders, sloping backs and elongated heads with horns pointing backwards. Males have a body weight of about 152 kg, while females are closer to 120 kg. They are typically found in open country, including grasslands, vleis, open woodlands and semi-desert bush savanna. They are common throughout the COH. Red hartebeest are predominantly grazers, also taking a very small amount of browse. They are gregarious and occur in herds ranging from 20 to 300 individuals, depending on the time of year. Males are territorial, controlling harem herds that consist of the male, several females and their offspring, plus some younger bulls.

Red hartebeest appeared very recently, and are therefore not known in the COH. Their fossils are known from Elandsfontein, Cornelia and Florisbad in South Africa, and from Kabwe in Zambia. The species probably has a similar time span to the black wildebeest, from 0,5 mya until the present.

EXTINCT GIANT WILDEBEEST
Megalotragus priscus

The giant wildebeest *Megalotragus* was possessed of enormous, sweeping horns, fragments of which are readily recognizable. Their body weight has been estimated at 534 kg, so they were larger than blue wildebeest, but not as massive as a bull eland. *Megalotragus* fossils are found throughout South Africa and East Africa, indicating that this animal had a wide distribution in the Plio-Pleistocene. The giant wildebeest is closely related to the blue wildebeest, which suggests that they occupied a similar habitat, namely open grasslands. They also had very high-crowned teeth, an adaptation seen in all grassland grazers, but not in browsers.

Megalotragus is found in Sterkfontein Member 4, Swartkrans Members 1–3, Kromdraai A, Gladysvale, Drimolen and Coopers. In

Red hartebeest

Extinct giant wildebeest

South Africa this species ranged from about 3 mya until approximately 12 000–10 000 years ago, when it became extinct.

BLESBOK
Damaliscus dorcas

The blesbok has a brown coat with white underbelly, and distinctive backward-curved horns. Male body weight is approximately 61 kg, while females are slightly smaller and lighter. Blesbok are endemic to South Africa, and are found throughout the COH. They are restricted to grasslands and require a nearby water source. They are predominantly grazers, and are partial to sprouting grasses, but will occasionally browse to supplement their diet. They are gregarious diurnal animals, with a social organization consisting of territorial males, female herds and bachelor groups. They normally stand facing the sun with their heads held low, but will begin to shake their heads up and down when approached.

Blesbok fossils are common in the COH, having been found in Sterkfontein Member 5, Swartkrans Members 1–3, Kromdraai A, Gladysvale, Drimolen and Coopers. This species ranges from about 1,5 mya until the present in South Africa alone.

Blesbok

EXTINCT BLESBOK
Damaliscus niro

Damaliscus niro was very similar to the modern blesbok except that it was larger and had slightly different horns. Its body weight was approximately 120 kg. Like the modern blesbok, *Damaliscus niro* was almost certainly an open grassland grazer, with a diet consisting almost exclusively of grass. It had high-crowned teeth and deep mandibles, and its skeleton was adapted for moving on relatively flat, open ground.

Damaliscus niro is found at Sterkfontein Member 5, Swartkrans Member 2 and possibly Gladysvale. *Damaliscus niro* ranged in time from about 2 mya until relatively recently, perhaps about 12 000 years ago, when it went extinct.

EXTINCT OVIBOVINE
Makapania broomi

This large, extinct bovid is remarkable in that its horns

Extinct blesbok

were positioned laterally. It has been referred to as an Ovibovine, making its closest living relatives the musk-ox of North America and the takin of Tibet. Its body weight is estimated to have been about 263 kg.

Makapania is thought to have been both a browser and a grazer. It probably preferred grasses, and would have required a nearby source of permanent water.

Makapania broomi has been found at Sterkfontein Members 4 and 5, Swartkrans Members 1–3, Gladysvale, Motsetse and possibly Coopers. It has been recovered from 3-million-year-old sediments in East Africa. The type specimen was found at Makapansgat. This species existed from about 3 mya until 1 mya, or perhaps more recently.

SPRINGBOK
Antidorcas marsupialis
Springbok are sleek, trim-looking animals, bright brown on top, white on the bottom with a black stripe down the side. Males weigh around 31 kg while females average 27 kg. They are restricted exclusively to South Africa and Botswana. Springbok are arid-adapted animals living in open grasslands and desert scrublands. They are mixed feeders, eating sprouting green grasses and herbs in the summer months and browsing on shrubs and trees in the winter months. Springbok are gregarious, living in small herds that in the past occasionally coalesced into vast herds of hundreds of thousands of animals. Males are territorial, while female herds generally wander in and out of male territories as they see fit. When suddenly alarmed, springbok will 'pronk', leaping up to 2 m in the air with the legs held stiffly downwards, repeating the move several times, possibly to signal danger to other members of the herd.

Springbok fossils are found at Swartkrans Members 1–3, Gladysvale, Motsetse, Coopers and possibly Sterkfontein Member 5. This species probably first appeared around 1,5 mya, and is still present in southern Africa today.

Springbok are found in most of the nature reserves in the COH.

Extinct ovibovine

EXTINCT SPRINGBOK
Antidorcas bondi
The extinct springbok, *Antidorcas bondi*, is somewhat

Springbok

smaller than the modern springbok, weighing on average about 25 kg. *Antidorcas bondi* was hyper-hypsodont, meaning that it had extremely high-crowned teeth. Its teeth are so high-crowned that the lower edge of its mandible is seriously distorted to fit the teeth. Such teeth are typically found in dedicated grazers, as they resist attrition to a greater extent than low-crowned teeth. Isotopic evidence also suggests that the diet of *Antidorcas bondi* was that of an exclusive grazer. It is possible that this small springbok followed larger antelope as they grazed, feeding on the new growth that sprouted up after the larger herbivores had moved through an area.

Antidorcas bondi has been recovered from Sterkfontein Member 4, Swartkrans Members 1–3, Kromdraai A and B, Gladysvale, Motsetse, Coopers and possibly Drimolen. This species therefore existed in South Africa from 2,5 mya until about 36 000 years ago, when it finally became extinct.

IMPALA

Aepyceros melampus

The impala is considered one of the most graceful antelopes in Africa, with a shiny, reddish-brown coat and long, slender legs. Impala are consistently associated with woodlands, particularly acacia and mopane. Cover and surface water are necessities. Impala are mixed feeders, including both browse and graze in their diet, depending on their locality and the time of year. They are gregarious, typically grouping together into small herds of 6–20 individuals, but aggregating into groups of 50–100 in the rainy season and early cold season. Males are territorial during the rutting season, generally grouping into bachelor herds. Territorial males will vigorously

Impala

defend female herds during the rut, sometimes resorting to head-pushing with interlocked horns.

Impala fossils are known from Gladysvale in the COH. They are also known in East Africa from about 2,5 mya, while impala fossils have been identified at Makapansgat, which extends the time range of this species from 3 mya until the present.

Impala are found in most nature reserves in the COH.

Klipspringer

KLIPSPRINGER

Oreotragus oreotragus

Klipspringers are small antelope with distinctive stiff, bristly hair that cushions them against bumps into rocks. Males tend to be smaller than females, the former weighing about 11 kg, while the latter average around 13 kg. Klipspringers are specifically evolved to occupy rocky habitats, requiring krantzes or koppies as suitable habitat. They are predominantly browsers, eating mostly leaves, berries, fruit, seed pods and flowers. Klipspringers are most commonly found in mated pairs, as solitary individuals, or in small family groups that include offspring. They walk on the very tips of their toes, hopping from rock to rock with tremendous agility. Klipspringers do not aggressively defend their territory from others, as most confrontations are resolved without violence.

Klipspringer fossils are known from Swartkrans Members 1–3, Gladysvale, Drimolen, Motsetse and Gondolin. The species can thus be traced from 3 mya until the present. However, they do not exist in the COH today.

CAPE BUFFALO

Syncerus caffer

Buffalo are extremely stocky, heavily built animals, and in old males the horns can grow to truly massive proportions. Males weigh on average near 700 kg, while females are somewhat smaller at 580 kg. They require a plentiful supply of grass, shade and water. They typically occupy woodlands, and avoid open grasslands or floodplains. Buffalo are grazers, preferring freshly sprouted grass, though they will just as readily feed on old grass. They are gregarious, occurring in relatively stable herds of up to several thousand individuals. Bulls maintain a strict hierarchy in the herd, and older individuals may be expelled. These old bulls are particularly vulnerable to lions. Buffalo are probably the most dangerous bovid in Africa. Their large horns can stop bullets, and wounded bulls have been known to circle hunters and attack from behind with great persistence.

Buffalo fossils are known from Swartkrans Members 1–3, Kromdraai A and Gladysvale. They are also known from East Africa, as early as 1,5 mya.

Buffalo

Their extremely high-crowned teeth signify that their diet was rich in grasses. Like modern buffalo, they were probably dedicated grazers, and dependent on water.

Giant buffalo fossils are found in Swartkrans Members 1 and 2, as well as Gladysvale. They first appeared in South Africa at Swartkrans about 1,5 mya, and survived until about 10 000 years ago, when they went extinct.

Buffalo probably first appeared about 1,5 mya, and continue to be found throughout Africa to the present.

In the COH, buffalo are found only in the Rhino & Lion Nature Reserve.

EXTINCT GIANT BUFFALO
Pelorovis antiquus

The giant buffalo was considerably larger than modern buffalo, with enormous horns stretching to as much as 3 m from tip to tip. Their body size may have exceeded 1 000 kg. The genus *Pelorovis* was found throughout East Africa and South Africa, though distinct species are known in the respective areas. The large size of the horns would have made movement in closed environments difficult, so it is probable that the giant buffalo preferred more open areas.

ELAND
Taurotragus oryx

Eland are the largest African antelope, with a brown coat and straight, spiralled horns. Bull eland weigh an average of 600 kg, and females 400 kg. They are equally at home in semi-desert scrublands and montane grasslands. Eland graze in summer and browse in winter. They can subsist in arid environments only if there is a sufficient quantity of

Extinct giant buffalo

Eland

succulent forage to replace permanent water sources. Eland are gregarious and usually occur in small herds, though they sometimes congregate in groups numbering up to 700 individuals. During the calving season females join together with yearlings and sub-adults in nursery herds, while the males associate together in independent herds.

Eland occupied a central place in the cosmology of the San and they are widely depicted in rock paintings throughout southern Africa.

Eland fossils are known from Sterkfontein Member 5, Swartkrans Members 2 and 3, Kromdraai A, Gladysvale and probably Coopers. The species has existed in South Africa from about 1,5 mya until the present.

Eland are found in most nature reserves in the COH.

KUDU
Tragelaphus strepsiceros

The kudu is one of the most magnificent antelope in Africa, with its remarkable spiralled horns and distinct white stripes on the face and sides. Male kudu weigh about 230 kg on average, and females around 160 kg. They are a savanna woodland species, avoiding desert, forest or open grassland areas. They are partial to areas of broken, rocky terrain with woodland cover and a nearby source of water. Kudu are predominantly browsers, though they may take fresh grass. They eat a wide variety of plants, preferring leaves and shoots but also taking seed pods. Kudu are gregarious, though herds rarely number more than 12 individuals, usually being closer to four or five individuals. They are mostly diurnal, but can adapt to nocturnal activity in disturbed areas (e.g. farming areas).

Kudu fossils are known from Sterkfontein Member 4, Swartkrans Members 1–3, Kromdraai A, Gladysvale and possibly Drimolen. They are also known in East Africa from about 2,5 mya, and can thus be traced from about 2,5 mya to the present in Africa.

Kudu are common throughout the COH.

Kudu

BUSHBUCK
Tragelaphus scriptus

Bushbuck are the smallest of the spiral-horned antelope, distinguished by their white stripes and spots. They weigh just under 50 kg, with females being slightly smaller than males. They are closely associated with riverine underbrush adjacent to permanent water supplies. Bushbuck are browsers, though they occasionally eat small quantities of grass. They are typically solitary animals, though they are sometimes seen in groups of two or three individuals. Bushbuck normally lie up in the daytime, feeding at night or twilight. They have excellent senses of sight, hearing and smell, and are extremely shy of humans. These factors allow them to live in close proximity to human developments in spite of hunting pressure. They are common throughout the COH.

Bushbuck fossils are known from Swartkrans Member 2 and Kromdraai A. They are known in East Africa from sites almost 3,5 million years of age, yet in South Africa they can only be traced back to about 1,5 million years.

SABLE

Hippotragus niger

Sable have a black, satiny coat with a pure white underside and long, backward-curved horns. Males weigh approximately 235 kg, and females about 220 kg. They are a savanna woodland species that require cover and available water. They prefer open woodlands adjacent to grasslands with medium to high grass. They are predominantly grazers, though they are known to browse to some extent. Sable are gregarious and occur in herds of 20–30 individuals, though they occasionally band together in groups of up to 200 animals. Their social organization consists of territorial bulls, nursery herds and bachelor groups. One or more females tend to dominate and lead the herd.

Sable fossils are known from Swartkrans Members 1–3, Kromdraai A, and possibly from Sterkfontein Members 4 and 5. Sable are known from at least 1,5 mya in South Africa, and perhaps even 2,5 mya.

Sable are found in several reserves throughout the COH.

GEMSBOK

Oryx gazella

Gemsbok are brown with a white underside and dark brown stripes on their sides, back and face, and have elongated, almost straight horns. Body weight in males averages 176 kg, and about 162 kg in females. They are well adapted to open, arid areas, preferring open grasslands, savanna bushlands or light, open woodlands. They are predominantly grazers, able to digest fibrous roughage, though they do

Sable

Waterbuck

switch to browse when transplanted out of their typical habitats. Gemsbok are gregarious and can be found in herds of up to 300 individuals. They occur in mixed herds, nursery herds and as solitary males. Gemsbok are not indigenous to the COH, having been transplanted into the area by humans. However, they are found in most reserves in the area.

Gemsbok fossils have never been recovered from the COH, most probably since their preferred environment did not exist in the area during the Plio-Pleistocene. The remains of gemsbok are unknown elsewhere in Africa.

WATERBUCK

Kobus ellipsiprymnus

Waterbuck have long horns that are swept back and upwards, and have thick brown hair and a broad white ring encircling the rump. Males weigh in the neighbourhood of 236 kg, and females about 186 kg. They are intimately associated with water, always being within a couple of kilometres of water at any given time. They are roughage feeders, grazing on a limited number of grasses and occsionally including a small amount of browse in their diet. Water buck are gregarious, usually occurring in herds of 6–12 individuals, but herds can sometimes number up to 30 animals. Social grouping consists of territorial males, nursery and bachelor herds.

Waterbuck fossils are rare in the COH, occurring only in Members 1 and 2 of Swartkrans. In South Africa they occur only from 1,5 mya to the present.

Waterbuck occur in most nature reserves in the COH.

MOUNTAIN REEDBUCK

Redunca fulvorufula

Mountain reedbuck are greyish in colour with a white underside and short, upturned horns. Males average about 30 kg in weight, while females are around 29 kg. Mountain reedbuck distribution is discontinuous as a result of their specialized habitat requirements. They tend to occupy stony grass-covered slopes of hills and mountains with tree or bush cover. They graze a very coarse, low-quality diet of specially selected grasses that vary seasonally. Mountain reedbuck are gregarious, and live in small groups of 3–8 individuals, and occasionally up to 40 individuals in certain seasons. Socially they are organized in groups of territorial males, non-territorial males, herds of females with young, and bachelor herds.

Mountain reedbuck are common in the COH today, although they are not known

Mountain reedbuck

in the fossil deposits of the COH, nor have they been recovered in East Africa. This probably stems from the fact that their preferred habitats are not conducive to fossilization. The ancestry and time range of this species is thus uncertain.

EXTINCT REEDBUCK
Redunca darti

The extinct reedbuck was slightly larger than the mountain reedbuck, weighing approximately 53 kg. The horns of this species were positioned differently to those of mountain reedbuck, arising more uprightly. The species was endemic to South Africa. The diet of *Redunca darti* probably comprised fresh grasses and was similar to, though not as specialized as, that of modern reedbuck. It was probably also quite dependent on water.

Redunca darti is known only from Gladysvale in the COH, although it has been tentatively identified at Coopers. It ranges in time from 3–2 mya, and perhaps younger.

LARGE RODENTS

Several species of large rodent that qualify as large-bodied mammals occur in the COH. A large-bodied mammal generally weighs more than 1 kg. The distinction between large-bodied and small-bodied mammals is important in terms of the collecting agents of fossil material in the area. Small-bodied mammals in the fossil caves were most likely brought into the caves by owls. Large-bodied mammals probably entered the caves of their own choice, or as the prey of a large mammalian carnivore.

SPRINGHARE
Pedetes capensis

The springhare is a rodent rather than an actual hare, resembling a miniature kangaroo more than anything else. Springhares weigh about 3 kg, and females are slightly smaller than males. Their most important habitat requirement is compacted sandy soil in which to dig their burrows. They are generally associated with open, grassy areas, avoiding areas with heavy cover. Springhares are grazers, subsisting almost entirely on grass. They are nocturnal, and very wary when out of their burrows. They have reason to be, as they are preyed upon by a wide variety of predators.

Springhare

Springhare fossils are known from Swartkrans Members 1–3 and Coopers, and may be present elsewhere in the COH as well. The genus *Pedetes* is at least 1,5 million years old.

PORCUPINE

Hystrix africaeaustralis

Modern porcupines are easily distinguished by their covering of sharp quills. They average about 12 kg in weight, with females being slightly larger than males. Porcupines have a wide habitat tolerance, existing in a variety of vegetational regimes. They display a marked preference for broken country with rocky hills and outcrops. Porcupines are adapted to digest a variety of foods, though they are mainly vegetarian. Their food includes bulbs, tubers and roots that they dig up. They live in extended family groups, comprising a male, female and successive generations of offspring. They occur in the wild in the COH.

Porcupine fossils are found at Sterkfontein Members 4 and 5, Swartkrans Members 1–3, Kromdraai A, Gladysvale, Motsetse and Coopers. They can be traced from 3 mya until today.

EXTINCT PORCUPINE

Hystrix makapanensis

The extinct porcupine was about a third larger than modern porcupines, weighing about 16 kg. *Hystrix makapanensis* probably had a diet similar to that of modern porcupines, though they may have eaten more grasses. They probably had a similarly wide habitat tolerance.

Hystrix makapanensis has been found in Swartkrans Member 1 and Kromdraai A. The species existed from 3 mya until at least 1,5 mya, if not until more recently.

Porcupine

Extinct porcupine

REPTILES

TORTOISES

LEOPARD TORTOISE

Geochelone pardalis

This tortoise weighs between 8 and 12 kg, but grows much larger in the Eastern Cape, where adults average 15–20 kg and may exceptionally exceed 70 cm in length and 40 kg in weight. The carapace is domed and not hinged, with the scutes not, or only faintly, raised. The beak is sometimes hooked, is unicuspid and often serrated. Each of the front feet has five claws. The carapace of hatchlings is yellow, with central paired or single black spots, the ground colour becoming darker and heavily blotched and streaked with black with age; old adults are often uniformly dark grey-brown. The plastron is yellowish, often with black radiating streaks and spots. Its habitat is varied.

Leopard tortoise

SNAKES

BROWN HOUSE SNAKE

Lamprophis fuliginosus

A large snake with a distinct head and small body scales. It is uniformly red-brown in colour. Large, old snakes are darker, almost black. There are two pale yellow streaks on the side of the head, which sometimes extend on to the front half of the body. The belly is off-white. The young sometimes have indistinct, pale lateral spots that may persist in adults. They grow to be about 60–90 cm, but may reach a maximum of 150 cm. These snakes forage for rodents and other small vertebrates at night. They are common in the COH.

Brown house snake

PUFF ADDER

Bitis arietanis

This thick, heavily built snake has a large, flattened, triangular head and large nostrils that point vertically upwards. The body is yellow-brown to light brown, with pale-edged, black chevrons on the back and bars on the tail. The belly is white or yellow, with a few scattered blotches. The male is smaller and more brightly coloured than the female. It grows to 70–90 cm in length, reaching a maximum of 120 cm. If disturbed, it adopts a striking posture and usually warns by giving a deep, hollow hiss. The venom is cytotoxic, often causing extensive swelling, pain and necrosis. These snakes are common in the COH.

Puff adder

RINKHALS

Hemachatus haemachatus

This stocky snake has a broad head and keeled scales in 17–19 rows. Coloration is varied. Some are conspicuously banded in dark brown to black, alternating with pale grey, yellowish or orange, while in others the back is uniformly dark brown to black, sometimes speckled with lighter greys and browns. The belly is dark, with one or two pale crossbands on the throat that may fade. It averages about 90–110 cm, reaching a maximum of 150 cm. The Rinkhals is a nocturnal species. It preys on most small vertebrates. In defence, it rears and spreads a broad hood. It can spray venom up to 2,5 m and usually aims it at the intruder's face. If this fails, it will sham death, rolling on to its back with the mouth agape. It is common in the COH.

MOZAMBIQUE SPITTING COBRA

Naja mossambica

A small cobra with a blunt head and 23–25 scale rows. The back is pale grey to dark olive above, with each scale edged in black. The belly is salmon pink to yellowish. There are irregular black cross-bands or blotches on the throat. It grows to an average of 90–120 cm, reaching a maximum of 150 cm. The spitting cobra is a nocturnal species. Its diet includes rodents, lizards, toads and grasshoppers. It produces copious amounts of dilute, neurotoxic venom that it sprays in the direction of intruders' eyes, causing agonizing and instant pain. It is common in the COH.

Spitting cobra

BOOMSLANG

Dispholidus typus

A large snake with a distinct head, and very large eyes with round pupils. Coloration is very variable. Juveniles are twig-coloured, often with blue spots on the forebody; the head is dark brown above and white below. They have emerald-green eyes and a yellow throat. Adult females are light olive or brown, with white to brown bellies. Males are more brightly coloured, and occur in various colour phases. They average 120–150 cm in length, though they can grow to 200 cm. These snakes are dangerous but reclusive. They hunt during the day. When cornered, these snakes will inflate their neck to expose the brightly coloured skin, and may strike. The venom is a potent haemotoxin. They are rare in the COH.

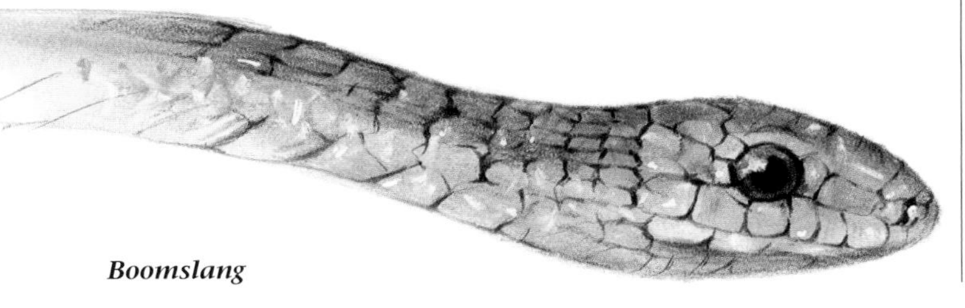

Boomslang

FROGS

GUTTURAL TOAD

Bufo gutturalis

Guttural toads are small with irregular, blotchy brown skin on the back and a white underbelly. They also have irregular red infusions on the backs of the thighs. They breed in open pools, dams, streams or other permanent water. They are commonly found in built-up areas. They feed on insects.

Guttural toad

BUBBLING KASSINA

Kassina senegalensis

Bubbling kassinas are small frogs with a distinct pattern of bold, dark stripes on a yellow back with a white underbelly.

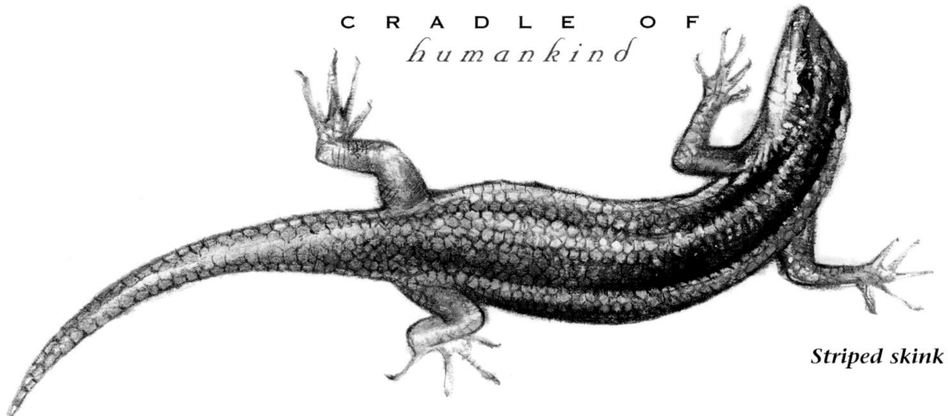

Striped skink

They breed in vleis, pans and dams in grassland areas. They tend to walk or run rather than hop.

Bubbling kassina

LIZARDS

STRIPED SKINK

Mabuya striata

This medium-sized skink has a window in each of its lower eyelids. There are spiny scales on the soles of the feet and a keel on the lamellae beneath the toes. The diet of this species includes most small insects. They are arboreal and common in the COH.

MONITORS

WATER MONITOR OR LEGUAAN

Varanus niloticus

This is one of the largest African lizards. It has a stout body with powerful limbs and strong claws. Monitors grow about 100–140 cm in size, but can reach up to 200 cm. The skin is covered with small, bead-like scales. The head has an elongated snout, and the nostrils are round and situated midway between the eyes and the end of the snout. The tail is much longer than the body. Adults are greyish brown to dirty olive-brown, with scattered darker blotches and light yellow ocelli and bands on the head, back and limbs. The belly and throat are paler, with black bars. The water monitor is common in the major river valleys of the COH. It is an excellent swimmer, using its long, oar-like tail to propel itself. It often basks on rock outcrops. Adults forage in freshwater pools for crabs, but will also take frogs, fish and birds and their eggs. Adults' teeth are rounded and peg-like.

GECKOS

CAPE DWARF GECKO

Lygodactylus capensis

A large dwarf gecko with a pair of lateral clefts in the mental (chin) and no soft spines above the eyes. The back is grey-brown, with a dark streak from the snout to the shoulder that sometimes extends on to the flank, and a pale dorsolateral

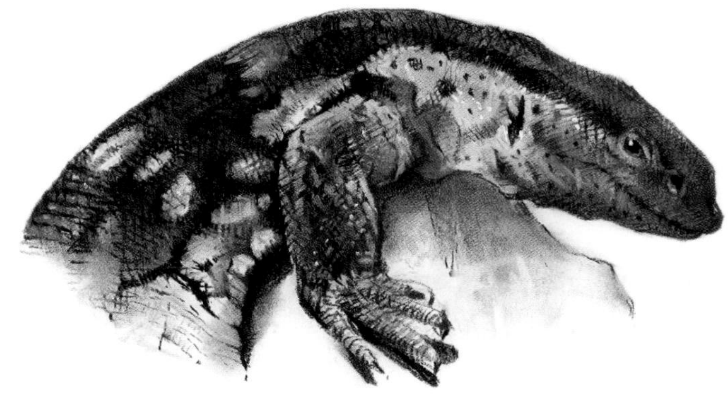

Water monitor

band that may break up into a series of light spots towards the tail. The throat is usually stippled with grey or dark brown. The belly is cream. They are found in low scrub and on dead trees, and feed almost exclusively on termites.

CHAMELEONS

FLAP-NECKED CHAMELEON

Chamaeleo dilepis

A large chameleon with a continuous crest on the throat and belly, a prehensile tail that is as long as the body, and occipital flaps. Coloration is varied, from pale yellow through shades of green to brown. The belly crest is white, and there is usually a pale bar and several white spots on the sides. The interstitial skin of the male throat pouch is orange. Diet consists of insects, particularly grasshoppers and beetles. It is easier to find at night, when it turns blue-white in colour. It is common in the COH.

BIRDS

This chapter comprises some 65 species representing the most commonly seen birds within the Cradle of Humankind, Gauteng. The following descriptions are a token representation of approximately 250 species hitherto recorded in the region. Birds that are rarely seen or difficult to see because of their habits or habitat type have been excluded, except where they represent high conservation status. A variety of habitats are found in the region, the main types being mosaic savanna, woodland, grassland, riverine and rocky hillside. Many of the bird species described here are closely associated with their preferred habitat, which can be an important aid to identification.

Both the revised 'internationally standardised' common names and the old names are mentioned in the text for the convenience of the reader.

Little Grebe

LITTLE GREBE (DABCHICK)

Tachybaptus ruficollis

A small, dark grebe with chestnut neck, dark cap and a diagnostic white patch at the base of the bill. It is most often found on open water bodies, often in pairs. Its call is a distinctive high-pitched 'trill'. Common resident within the COH. 23–29 cm

REED CORMORANT

Phalacrocorax africanus

A slender black cormorant, with pale speckling on the wings. Males have a small crest on the forehead. Adults have orange-yellow facial skin and red eyes. They usually occur singly on freshwater dams and lakes. Common resident within the COH. 50–55 cm

CATTLE EGRET

Bubulcus ibis

Buff feathers and a short red bill present on breeding adults. Legs range from yellow to dark brown, and orange at the start of the breeding season; feet black. Loose flocks often seen in association with cattle and game, large numbers when breeding. Common resident in the COH. 50–56 cm

Cattle Egret

HADEDA IBIS
Bostrychia hagedash
A heavy-bodied grey-brown bird, with iridescent pink shoulders at close range. Grey face with white cheek-stripes. Long, dark, decurved bill and short legs. Usually in pairs or small groups on moist ground, in a wide range of habitats. Raucous when perched or in flight, uttering a loud 'Ha! Ha-ha da-da'. Roosts in tall trees at night. 76–89 cm

Hadeda Ibis

AFRICAN SACRED IBIS
Threskiornis aethiopicus
Black unfeathered head, neck and legs, white body and a long decurved black bill. In flight the feathers are black-tipped. Flocks or loose groups forage on farmland or marshy areas. Groups may often be seen flying in a V-formation. Common resident within the COH. 64–82 cm

Egyptian Goose

EGYPTIAN GOOSE
Alopochen aegyptiaca
Large brown body with rufous eye-patch and brown patch on the chest. Bill and legs are pink. Pairs inhabit freshwater lakes and feed in fields. Noisy when interacting together. Common resident within the COH. 63–73 cm

YELLOW-BILLED DUCK
Anus undulata
Bright yellow bill with central black patch which is diagnostic. Feathers are brown-edged with white, lighter in colour than that of the African Black Duck, which also occurs in the area. In flight shows bright green speculum. Occurs on most freshwater lakes in the COH; seen in pairs or small flocks. Common resident within the COH. 51–58 cm

Yellow-billed Duck

CAPE VULTURE
Gyps coprotheres
A pale vulture, with a honey-coloured eye. Similar to, but

Cape Vulture

larger than the White-backed Vulture. Dark flight feathers contrast with pale wing linings in flight. Regularly seen sitting on power lines in the COH. It breeds on cliffs in the Magaliesberg and occurs in grassland habitats. Its status is threatened, despite being endemic to the region. 100–115 cm

STEPPE BUZZARD
Buteo vulpinus
The plumage is variable, ranging from dark brown, to russet, to pale. Diagnostic in most forms is a distinct pale band across the breast. Flanks are usually barred. It is frequently seen perched on roadside telephone poles in open country. Common summer visitor to the COH. 45–50 cm

BLACK-SHOULDERED KITE
Elanus caeruleus
Distinctive, easily identified grey and white raptor with diagnostic black shoulder patches and ruby red eyes. It is graceful in flight and has a characteristic habit of hovering. Often seen perched on telephone poles and lines in open countryside, often wagging its white tail up and down while watching the ground. Common resident with local movements within the COH. 33 cm

Black-shouldered Kite

HELMETED GUINEAFOWL
Numida meleagris
Dark grey body with white flecks. Naked blue head, red cap and horny casque are diagnostic in this large game bird. Immature birds are largely brown. They occur in grassland and agricultural land in large flocks, except when breeding. Call is a repeated 'ker-tek-ker-tek-ker-tek-chrrrr'. Common resident within the COH. 58–64 cm

Helmeted Guineafowl

COMMON MOORHEN
Gallinula chloropus
Sooty black with a bright red bill, tipped with yellow, and greenish-yellow legs. Frequents almost any stretch of open water with reed fringes. Prefers to swim in open water. Call a sharp 'kr-rrrk'. Common resident within the COH. 30–36 cm

BARROW'S (SOUTHERN WHITEBELLIED) KORHAAN
Eupodotis barrowii
A small, pale korhaan, the male having a diagnostic dark cap, blue-grey neck and breast and white belly. The Northern Black Korhaan has a black belly and conspicuous white flashes in the primaries in flight. Pairs or small groups can be found in open grassland. It is an endemic, uncommon resident within the COH. 52–61 cm

CROWNED LAPWING (PLOVER)
Vanellus coronatus
A large plover with a black cap and surrounding white circle, pale yellow eye, red bill and legs. Occurs in short, dry grassland and fallow fields, also on golf courses and playing fields, often in small flocks. May be seen with

Crowned Lapwing

Black-winged Lapwing. A noisy species, calling 'kriek-k kriek-k' repeatedly. Common resident within the COH. 30–31 cm

AFRICAN WATTLED LAPWING (PLOVER)
Vanellus senegallus
Largest lapwing of the region. Bright yellow bill, wattles and legs, and brown breast and underparts. The call is a high pitched 'kweep-kweep'; regularly calls at night. Occurs usually in pairs in damp grassland, riverbanks and vleis. Fairly common resident within the COH. 35 cm

BLACKSMITH LAPWING (PLOVER)
Vanellus armatus
Large pied plover with grey wings, black bill and legs; its bold pattern makes it easily distinguishable in flight. Call is a loud metallic 'tink, tink, tink' alarm call. Usually seen in pairs in a variety of damp areas. Common resident within the COH. 31 cm

SPOTTED THICK-KNEE (DIKKOP)
Burhinus capensis
This species has heavily spotted underparts, displaying two small white patches on each upperwing when in flight. It is largely nocturnal, and rests by day under bushes. It prefers dry, sparse bush and rocky, grazed areas, and is a fairly common resident within the COH. 43 cm

Spotted Thick-knee

RED-EYED DOVE
Streptopelia semitorquata
Grey-pink head and red eye and eye-ring are diagnostic features of this dove. In flight it shows grey outer tail feathers. The breast is a deeper pink than the pale grey breast of the Cape Turtle Dove. Call is a 'coo-coo'. Occurs in a variety of habitats from dry bushveld to riverine forests. Common resident within the COH. 30–33 cm

LAUGHING DOVE
Streptopelia senegalensis
No black collar is present in this species; has rather a small pinkish head and light black flecks across its pink breast. In flight the blue-grey forewings contrast strongly with the cinnamon back, and the white outer tail feathers are conspicuous. Call is a soft 'coo-cooc-cook-coo-coo'. It is

Red-eyed Dove

found in a wide variety of habitats and is a common resident throughout the COH. 22–24 cm

GREY GO-AWAY-BIRD (LOURIE)
Corythaixoides concolor
Uniform grey bird with long tail and pronounced crest. It occurs in pairs and small parties in mixed woodland and thornveld. It is highly vocal with a harsh nasal 'ko-whaaaay'. Flies with heavy movements, and is often seen perched comically atop thorn trees. Common resident within the COH. 48 cm

Grey Go-away-bird

RED-CHESTED CUCKOO
Cuculus solitarius
Diagnostic broad russet upper breast. Juveniles have dark grey head and upperparts. This species is very difficult to locate, as it sits quietly in thick canopy. The well-known, frequently repeated 'whit-weet-weooo' ('piet-my-vrou') call gives away its presence. It occurs in a variety of wooded habitats including gardens, and is a common summer visitor to the COH. 28–31 cm

BURCHELL'S COUCAL
Centropus burchelli
Black cap, rufous back, creamy breast and underparts, and fine rufous barring on the rump. This secretive species occurs singly or in pairs in reeds, dense thickets and long grass. It has a distinctive bubbling call 'doo-doo-dooo-doo-doo-doo', descending in scale, rising at the end. Fairly common resident within the COH. 40–41 cm

AFRICAN PALM-SWIFT
Cypsiurus parvus
The most slender and streamlined of all the swifts, long, deeply forked tail and uniform grey-brown colour are diagnostic. Occurs in small flocks, sometimes in the company of other species of swifts, flying rapidly in the vicinity of palm trees both in towns and open areas. Common resident within the COH. 17 cm

African Palm Swift

SPECKLED MOUSEBIRD
Colius striatus
This species is distinguished from the Red-faced Mousebird also found in the region by its drabber brown coloration, black facial patch and dark

Speckled Mousebird

upper mandible and white lower mandible. It has a weak flight action and is often seen in flocks following each other from one bush clump to another. It prefers dense bush, forest fringes and gardens. Common resident within the COH. 35 cm

PIED KINGFISHER
Ceryle rudis
Entirely black and white, the male having a double black breast band, the female an incomplete breast band. It occurs in small groups on rivers or dams, frequently hovering over open water while fishing. The highly vocal call is a high-pitched twittering, often by two or more birds at the same time. Common resident within the COH. 23–25 cm

HALF-COLLARED KINGFISHER
Alcedo semitorquata
Slightly larger than the Malachite Kingfisher, but differentiated by its black bill and blue cheeks. A secretive, jewel-like kingfisher, inhabiting wooded streams and usually seen perching on a low overhanging branch, bobbing its head rapidly. It has a high-pitched 'chreep' call when in flight. A fairly common resident within the COH. Its habitat in southern Africa is highly threatened. 18–20 cm

Half-collared Kingfisher

EUROPEAN BEE-EATER
Merops apiaster
Chestnut crown and mantle, yellow back and throat, turquoise-blue head and breast. Occurs in a wide range of habitats, often heard calling from high overhead, a characteristic liquid 'krrup, krrup' call. Groups may often be seen sitting on roadside telephone wires in the COH region. Common summer visitor. 26–28 cm

European Bee-eater

AFRICAN GREY HORNBILL
Tockus nasutus
The only small hornbill in the area. It has a dark bill and a creamy stripe at the base. Female bill has an orange tip and pale upper mandible. They prefer mixed bushveld and broad-leaved woodland. Call is a thin plaintive 'phe-phephee-phe-phe pheeoo-pheeooo'. Mainly arboreal. Increasingly common resident within the COH. 46–51 cm

African Grey Hornbill

GREEN (REDBILLED) WOOD-HOOPOE
Phoeniculus purpureus
Long decurved red bill and red legs, white wing bars and a long tail. Occurs in small parties in woodland or mature gardens, flying from tree to tree in a loose fashion, feeding low in the canopy before moving on. Call is a high-pitched chattering uttered by several of the group, becoming a hysterical cacophony of sound. Common resident in the COH. 32–36 cm

AFRICAN HOOPOE
Upupa africana
Long decurved bill, and black-tipped crest which is raised when alarmed. Cinnamon-coloured body and black and white barred wings are striking in flight. Occurs in open, broad-leaved woodland, parks and gardens. Call is a simple 'hoop-hoop-hoop'. Often terrestrial, seen singly or in pairs. Common resident in the COH. 25–28 cm

African Hoopoe

CRESTED BARBET
Trachyphonus vaillantii
Yellow face speckled with red, small black crest and broad black breast band are diagnostic. They occur singly or in pairs in a variety of woodland, savanna and riverine habitats. The male call is a continuous trilling 'trrrrrr....'. Common resident within the COH. 23–24 cm

Lesser Striped Swallow

LESSER STRIPED SWALLOW
Hirundo abyssinica
Smaller and more heavily streaked than the Greater Striped Swallow (also common within the region) and the rufous cap extends over the ear coverts. Usually found near water and bridges, flying actively in pursuit of aerial insects. Perches on telephone wires and trees. Common summer visitor to the COH. 15–17 cm

BARN (EUROPEAN) SWALLOW
Hirundo rustica
Rufous forehead and throat, and dark blue breast band are diagnostic. Underparts are creamy. Moulting birds often lack long tail streamers. Occurs in most habitats, in larger numbers than any other swallow in summer. Call is a soft twittering sound, particularly when roosting in reedbeds. Large flocks perch on telephone wires. Abundant summer visitor to the COH. 15–18 cm

FORK-TAILED DRONGO
Dicrurus adsimilis
Easily recognised by its deeply forked tail, red eye and all-black plumage. It occurs in woodland and savanna, preferring an open park-like habitat, where it may be seen perched, frequently dropping to catch insects on the ground. Noisy and aggressive in behaviour, it is a fairly common resident within the COH. 23–26 cm

Fork-tailed Drongo

BLACK-HEADED (EASTERN) ORIOLE

Oriolus larvatus

Its black head (diagnostic), red bill and yellow plumage make this species visually striking. Seen singly or in pairs in mature woodland, mixed bushveld and exotic plantations. The call is a liquid whistle 'phoodleeoo'. Common resident within the COH. 22–22 cm

PIED CROW

Corvus albus

A large black bird with a white belly and collar. Occurs widely where there is human habitation, scavenging on food scraps of any variety. Call is a loud 'kraak'. It is a common resident in the COH, usually seen singly or in pairs. 46–50 cm

Pied Crow

DARK-CAPPED (BLACK-EYED) BULBUL

Pycnonotus tricolor

Dark crested head, black eye and yellow vent. This is a gregarious species inhabiting bushveld, riverine forest, gardens and thornveld. Several cheerful calls can be frequently heard. Abundant resident within the COH. 19–22 cm

Dark-capped Bulbul

KAROO THRUSH

Turdus smithi

This species is much darker above than the Olive Thrush, and has a grey, not white vent. Seen singly or in pairs in woodland, parks and gardens. Males drop their wings and splay out their tail when displaying. Common within the COH. An endemic resident to the region. 20–22 cm

Karoo Thrush

FAMILIAR CHAT

Cercomela familiaris

A small, pale brown bird, with a rich chestnut rump and outer tail feathers. Wing feathers have a buffy edge. Often flicks its wings while perched. It occurs on rocky terrain and near farm buildings and is tame and confiding. Its call is a warbling trill. Common resident within the COH. 14–15 cm

CAPPED WHEATEAR

Oenanthe pileata

A striking species with a white forehead and eyebrow, and a black cap and breast band. The white throat and belly are distinctive in the field. Frequents bare stony ground and stunted grassveld. Sometimes seen in loose groups walking about with much tail and wing flicking. Common resident with local movements within the COH. 17–18 cm

AFRICAN (COMMON) STONECHAT
Saxicola torquatus
Male has a black head, white patch on the neck and a dark rufous breast. Female is plainer with a pale grey head. Its habitat preference is open grassland, vleis, roadsides and dams. Usually seen in pairs, its call is a high-pitched warble. It is a common resident with local movements within the COH. 13–14 cm

MOCKING CLIFF-CHAT
Thamnolaea cinnamomeiventris
The black plumage, deep chestnut belly and rump and white shoulder patch of the male are diagnostic. The female has grey upperparts. They occur in pairs on bushy, rocky slopes and around cave entrances. The song is a melodious mix involving imitations of other birdcalls. Lively and active birds common all year round within the COH. 19–21 cm

Mocking Cliff-Chat

CAPE ROBIN-CHAT (ROBIN)
Cossypha caffra
White eyebrows, orange throat and upper breast, belly and undertail coverts. Pale grey lower breast and dark back. Occurring along forest edges, riverine vegetation, bushveld and gardens. A sweet, melodious song, starting with 'cheroo-weet-weet-weet'. Common resident within the COH. 16–17 cm

Cape Robin-Chat

(CAPE REED) LESSER SWAMP-WARBLER
Acrocephalus gracilirostris
This warbler has a distinct white eyebrow stripe. The bill is long and strong and the legs are dark brown. The call is a distinctively rich and melodious 'cheerup-chee-tirririririr'. Its favoured habitat is fresh water in bulrushes and reedbeds. It is a common resident within the COH. 14–16 cm

ZITTING (FANTAILED) CISTICOLA
Cisticola juncidis
The tail of this small brown-streaked bird is more marked than in other cisticolas, and the white-tipped tail is distinctive. They are conspicuous only during summer when displaying males cruise high up in a dipping flight pattern, calling a repeated 'zit' at the crest of each undulation. They occur in rich grassland, often in damp areas. A common resident within the grasslands of the COH. 10 cm

NEDDICKY
Cisticola fulvicapilla
The rufous cap and plain brown upperparts help in identifying this cisticola. Usually seen in pairs or small groups in the lower stratum of mosaic grassland and savanna. During summer the song is an often repeated 'tseep-tseep-tseep'. 11 cm

TAWNY-FLANKED PRINIA
Prinia subflava
Identified by its clear white underparts, cream eye-stripe, tawny flanks and rufous wing-edges. Usually occurring in riverine vegetation and rank grassveld, often in noisy groups of four to six. The call

is a rapid, continuous 'przzt-przzt-przzt'. A common resident within the COH. 11–12 cm

AFRICAN PARADISE-FLYCATCHER
Terpsiphone viridis
This striking species is unmistakable with its dark head, bright blue bill and eye-ring, and orange-brown back and tail. The male loses its tail in the non-breeding season. Occurs in riverine forest, bush and mature gardens. They are highly active, often heard calling 'twee-tiddly-te-te'. They are breeding summer visitors to the COH. 17–20 cm (plus 18 cm tail in breeding male)

African Paradise-Flycatcher

CAPE WHITE-EYE
Zosterops capensis
A small, active species with greenish underparts, white eye-ring and green back and crown. Occurs in most wooded habitats including savanna and gardens. The call is a soft, often-heard 'tweee-tuuu-tweee-twee'. Common resident within the COH. Endemic to the region. 12 cm

Cape White-eye

CHINSPOT BATIS
Batis molitor
Males are black and white with a narrow breast band, white underparts and grey head. Females have a clear rufous chin-spot and breast band. Frequents dry woodland and thornveld, often in pairs. The call is a characteristic, descending 'teuu-teuu-teuu'. A common resident within the COH. 13 cm

CAPE WAGTAIL
Motacilla capensis
Plain greyish upperparts and pale white underparts with a narrow breast band are diagnostic in this species. May be located near fresh water, gardens and open savanna, walking and feeding on the ground singly or in pairs. The call is a clear and strident 'tsee-chee-chee'. A common resident within the COH. 19–20 cm

AFRICAN (GRASSVELD) PIPIT
Anthus cinnamomeus
This terrestrial species can be identified by the yellow base to its bill, strong facial markings and white (not buffy) outer tail feathers. It has bold streaking on the breast and a slightly streaked back. It occurs in any type of grassland, taking off when disturbed with a 'trrit-trrit-trrit' call and a characteristic 'dipping' flight pattern. A common resident within the COH. 16–17 cm

CAPE (ORANGE-THROATED) LONGCLAW
Macronyx capensis
The deep orange throat encircled with black and yellow underparts is diagnostic in this terrestrial species. Has an upright stance, and is often seen atop a termite mound or slight rise. Occurs singly or in pairs in grassland. When disturbed flies a short way uttering its melodious song, 'cheewit-cheewit'. Common resident within the COH. Endemic to the region. 20 cm

Cape Longclaw

COMMON FISCAL (FISCAL SHRIKE)
Lanius collaris
A heavy-bodied black and white bird with a strong bill. The white outer tail feathers are diagnostic. Female has a rufous patch on the flanks.

Common Fiscal

They occur in almost all habitats except forest, are bold and may often be seen perching conspicuously on a branch or fence post, flying down to catch prey from the ground. The call is a harsh 'skiza, skiza' or mixed mimicry of other birds' calls. Common resident within the COH. 21–23 cm

SOUTHERN BOUBOU
Laniarius ferrugineus
A strong bird with black upperparts, creamy throat and rufous belly. Its preferred habitat is riverine thicket. It is a skulking, secretive bird, preferring the lower stratum in dense bush. The call is a variable duet, the most frequently heard notes being 'boo-boo' with a whistled 'whee-ooo' in reply. A common resident within the COH.
20–22 cm

BLACK-BACKED PUFFBACK
Dryoscopus cubla
A small black and white bird, with white wing coverts and ruby-red eyes. The large white rump in the male is highly conspicuous when puffed up and spread out during display. Pairs, regularly seen in mixed bird parties, favour mixed woodland and forest. The call is a sharp, repeated 'chik-weeu, chik-weeu!' Common resident within the COH.
16–18 cm

CAPE GLOSSY STARLING
Lamprotornis nitens
A uniformly glossy blue-green plumage, in poor light appears duller blue-black. Occurs in a variety of mixed thornveld and woodland, and increasingly in suburbia. The call is a cheerful 'Trr-treer-chree-chrrrr'. Usually seen in pairs, and is a common resident within the COH. 25 cm

Cape Glossy Starling

RED-WINGED STARLING
Onychognathus morio
A dark blue-black starling with dark eyes and red-brown flight feathers. Inhabits rocky hillsides, caves or farm buildings

Red-winged Starling

where it roosts. Characteristically bold, often heard while in flight by its clear, loud, whistled 'cher-leeeeeoo'. Highly common resident within the COH. 27–30 cm

(AFRICAN) PIED STARLING
Spreo bicolor
A large, dark brown starling identified by its white vent and belly, bright creamy white eye, yellow gape and long legs. It may be found in grassland, often around farm buildings, and along the roadside. Call is a soft 'skeer-kerra-kerra'. Fairly common within the COH. Endemic to the region. 27–28 cm

Pied Starling

GREATER DOUBLE-COLLARED SUNBIRD
Cinnyris afer
Long, decurved bill, broad red breast band and iridescent green upperparts. Female has grey-brown upperparts, paler below. Pairs may be found near valley bush and forest fringes. Song is a loud, fast and frequently repeated 'tchut-tchut-tchut'. Fairly common within the COH. Endemic to the region. 14 cm

Greater Doubled-collared Sunbird

SOUTHERN GREY-HEADED SPARROW
Passer diffusus
The plain grey head and single white wing bar, chestnut rump, back and wings render this sparrow unmistakable. It occurs in a variety of wooded habitats, including suburbia. Pairs and small flocks may frequent large bare trees or be seen feeding on the ground. Common resident within the COH. 15 cm

SOUTHERN MASKED-WEAVER
Ploceus velatus
The black mask extends to the forehead, and down towards the throat. Breeding males have red eyes, plain back and brown legs. Females have a brown eye and streaked back. Non-breeding males resemble females but have a red eye. Occurs in riverine bush, savanna and grassland. Breeds colonially near water. Gregarious at all times. Common resident within the COH. 11–14.5 cm

Southern Masked-Weaver

Long-tailed Widowbird

SOUTHERN RED BISHOP

Euplectes orix

Black forehead and belly, and bright red upper breast and back. Primaries are brown. Usually associated with water; however ranges into grassland and savanna. Occurs in large flocks, breeding in reedbeds. Highly gregarious species, in breeding male call is a buzzing, chirping song. In winter, flocks become nomadic. Common resident within the COH. 10–11 cm

Southern Red Bishop

LONG-TAILED WIDOWBIRD (WIDOW)

Euplectes progne

The largest widowbird in the region. Breeding males distinguished by long heavy tail, and the bright red shoulder patch and pale bill. Females and non-breeding males have red shoulder patch and buff stripe below. Occurs in open grassland, near vleis and in valleys. Breeding males perch conspicuously or may be seen flying low and on heavy wings, within their territory. Common resident within the COH. m=19 cm (plus 40 cm tail), f=16 cm

COMMON WAXBILL

Estrilda astrild

The red bill and eye stripe and pink underbelly are distinctive features of this small, brownish, long-tailed finch. This gregarious species is commonly found in long grass, reedbeds, and rank vegetation bordering cultivated lands. Usually seen in large flocks moving in a loose fashion from one feeding area to another. Call is a nasal 'cher-cher-cher'. Common resident within the COH. 11–12 cm

CINNAMON-BREASTED (ROCK) BUNTING

Emberiza tahapisi

This small bunting may be recognised by its cinnamon colouring, dark throat and a strong black and white streaked head. Usually occurs in pairs on rocky or stony terrain, eroded plains and mixed bushveld. The call is a distinctive rattling song, 'chirri-chee'. Common resident, although nomadic within the COH when not breeding. 14–15 cm

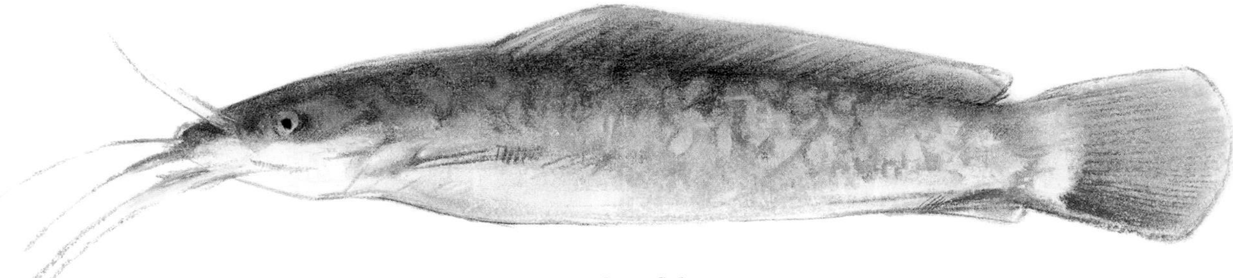

Rock catfish

FISH

ROCK CATFISH
Austroglanis sclateri
This fish is olive-brown with scattered spots, fleshy lips and three pairs of short barbels. It lives in rocky habitats in flowing water, favouring rapids.

BROAD-STRIPED BARB
Barbus annectens
This is a translucent olive-brown fish with either three spots or a broad dark band along its body. It also has a dark spot at the base of the anal fin. It favours slow-flowing streams that have significant vegetation.

SMALL-SCALE YELLOWFISH
Barbus polylepis
This fish is olive-bronze above, and cream below. The lips tend to be variable, from thin to fleshy. It inhabits clear flowing waters of streams and dams in the COH.

BANDED TILAPIA
Tilapia sparrmanii
This is a deep olive-green fish with eight or nine vertical bars on its body and two bars between the eyes. It also has the distinguishing 'tilapia spot' on the dorsal fin. It prefers quiet or standing waters. The males construct nests in which eggs are guarded by both parents.

MOZAMBIQUE TILAPIA
Oreochromis mossambicus
This fish is silvery olive to deep blue-grey, and its dorsal and caudal fins have red margins. Breeding males turn grey-black with a white lower head and throat. This fish occurs in all but fast-flowing waters. The male constructs a saucer-shaped nest, and the female mouth-broods.

CARP
Cyprinus carpio
This is an olive-brown to rich gold fish, with grey fins. Its dorsal and anal fins have a serrated spine. It may be partly naked with scattered scales, or without scales. It favours large bodies of slow-flowing or standing water. As an introduced species, it is now widespread in the COH.

Mozambique tilapia

INSECTS AND ARACHNIDS

Baboon spider

COMMON BABOON SPIDER
***Harpactira* sp.**
These spiders are heavily built with thick legs and long, leg-like pedipalps. They tend to be dark brown to black. Their spinnerets protrude beyond their abdomen, and they live in silk-lined burrows.

BANDED-LEGGED GOLDEN ORB-WEB SPIDER
Nephila senegalensis
This spider has a cylindrical abdomen with black and yellow markings. Its carapace is brown with silvery hair. Its legs are banded black and yellow with 'hair' tufts on three pairs. It hangs in a large web of golden silk surrounded by trip lines. Its webs attract dew in the mornings, and shine a brilliant gold in the early morning sunlight.

RAIN SPIDER
***Palystes* sp.**
These spiders are greyish with slightly darker markings on the abdomen. The legs are banded yellow and dark brown underneath. They build tennis ball-sized dried leaf nests for their eggs in vegetation. They are nocturnal, free-range hunters that often come indoors. They can grow very large, reaching the size of a small person's hand.

Rain spider

BLACK ROCK SCORPION
***Hadogenes* sp.**
These scorpions are blackish brown and flattened. They have medium-sized pincers and a long thin tail. The venom is not particularly dangerous to humans. They live in crevices in rocky areas.

SOLIFUGIDS
Order *Solifugae*
Although similar in appearance, these animals are actually not spiders. They have a hairy body in two parts, a massive, hard head with formidable toothed jaws and a soft, segmented abdomen. They are swift, voracious hunters that kill their prey without venom and digest them internally. They dig burrows and are widespread in hot, dry areas. Larger solifugids are capable of killing large animals such as birds.

Solifuge

COMMON TERMITES
***Trinervetermes* sp.**
Common termites are soft-bodied with a reddish-brown head and pale abdomen. Colonies include reproductives, a queen, workers and soldiers. Their mouthparts are large and tend to be pincer-like in soldiers. They tend to build bald, hemispherical mounds about 30 cm high. Winged imagoes ('flying ants') emerge after rain, fly a short distance, shed their wings and attract mates with their pheromones. They taste like herbs, and may have formed an important part of the diet of early hominins.

KING CRICKETS (PARKTOWN PRAWNS)
Family Stenopelmatidae
These large insects are reddish brown, have long antennae and are covered in spines. They are omnivorous and nocturnal, and produce a foul-smelling faecal discharge if disturbed. They inhabit gardens and beaches in warmer regions, and all too often enter homes.

PLANTS

Despite the harshness of the underlying bedrock, the COH (Cradle of Humankind) supports a unique and diverse floral community. Several hundred plant species are found here, making this one of the most diverse plant communities in the world, second only to the Cape fynbos. The COH vegetation is described either as 'Bankenveld' or 'Rocky Highveld Grassland'. The area is an important conservation zone for grassland, which is threatened by urban development. Less than three per cent of this vegetation type is properly protected in Gauteng. Best places in the COH to view the large indigenous gallery forests that have remained unchanged for hundreds of years, and gain a sense of the prehistoric bush in which our ancestors lived, are the extensive John Nash Nature Reserve, Plover's Lake and the Mogale's Gate Reserve.

WILD FLOWERS

BUSHMAN POISON BULB

Boophane disticha

The bulb of this plant protrudes well above the ground, with leaves up to 30 cm long arranged in a fan. The flower stalks reach up to 30 cm in length, and the seeds are enclosed at the ends of the stalks. The large, dry fruiting head can be up to 60 cm in diameter, and breaks loose, rolling in the wind. It is widespread in the COH.

Bushman poison bulb

WILD MORNING GLORY

Ipomoea crassipes

This is a prostrate or scrambling creeper with purple flowers reaching up to 7 cm in diameter. The leaves have yellowish hairs and are

Wild morning glory

held erect. It flowers from November to February, and its fruit splits open as it matures. It is widespread in the grasslands of the COH.

WILD SWEETPEA
Sphenostylis angustifolia
This low-growing shrub reaches about 40 cm in height.

Wild sweetpea

The flowers are found on the stem, held above the leaves. It produces a scent from October to January. It is found on rocky hillsides and grasslands. It is widespread in the COH.

STAR FLOWER
Hypoxis hemerocallidea
This perennial forb stands up to 25 cm high, with large flowers from September to January. The bulb has a fibrous outer layer; the leaves are found in three ranks. Widespread in grassland areas, it is sought after as a medicinal plant.

SPIDER ORCHID
Bonatea speciosa
This is a robust plant that can grow up to 1 m tall. The leaves are moderate sized and there is a large inflorescence. The flowers are about 8 cm long with a trilobed tip and long spur. It is common in the COH.

Star flower

Spider orchid

PYJAMA FLOWER
Androcymbium melanthioides
This low-growing bulbous plant is characterized by broad pinkish-green bracts with distinctive parallel venation. The small yellow flowers are arranged in the centre of the plant and are observed in the autumn and winter months. It is found in grassland areas.

Pyjama flower

White lady

WHITE LADY

Kalanchoe thyrsiflora

This is a perennial succulent plant that grows from 70 to 100 cm in height. The leaves are densely packed, spoon-shaped and green with a white frosting of colour. The flowers bloom yellow. It prefers full sunlight, in dry to moist soil. It tends to be found in scrub and lightly wooded areas in the COH.

BOBBEJAANKOMKOMMER

Trochomeria macrocarpa

This is a small cucurbit with an elongated caudex. It has a large, fleshy root stock, short stems and elegant, long-petalled green flowers. It is native to South Africa, and can be found in grassland and lightly wooded areas of the COH.

Bobbejaankomkommer

Wild penstemon

WILD PENSTEMON

Graderia subintegra

These low-growing forbs reach about 600 mm in height. The flowers grow up to 30 mm in diameter and bloom from September to November. They are found in grasslands and rocky outcrops of the COH.

LARGE WITCHWEED

Striga elegans

These plants grow to about 30 cm tall, and have bright green stalks and leaves. The flowers are normally bright red, but may also grow white or yellow. They bloom from October to February.

Large witchweed

Witchweed is a parasitic plant that can be very destructive to food crops such as mealies and sorghum.

KERRIEBLOM

Gnidia capitata

This shrublet is evergreen and grows up to 40 cm high. The bark is brown to grey and smooth. The leaves are blue-green and the flowers mustard yellow. The fruits are very small and inconspicuous. It is found in grassland and flowers in spring. This branching shrublet is conspicuous after fires, and has been used as a traditional headache cure and as a divining torch to unmask thieves.

Kerrieblom

MONKEY'S TAIL

Xerophyta retinervis

These plants grow to about 1,2 m tall, with fibrous black stems. The grass-like leaves can reach 2,5 m in length. The flowers are blue or purple-pink and scented, blooming from August to October. It is found in hot, dry areas on rocky hillsides, and is widespread throughout the COH.

Monkey's tail

GLADIOLUS

Gladiolus elliotii

These plants grow to about 800 mm in length. The flowers range in colour from white to milky blue with yellow markings on the lower petals, and are usually rather open and tend to droop. They bloom in summer and occur mostly in grasslands in the COH.

Gladiolus

Common poison-bush flowers

TREES

COMMON POISON-BUSH

Acokanthera oppositifolia

This tree has upright branches, and stands between 2 and 7 m in height. The leaves are thick and leathery, with distinct side veins and a sharp tip. It flowers between June and October, with a red fruit that ripens to black. It is found in riverine areas in the COH.

Small aloe

Nana-berry

SMALL ALOE

Aloe greatheadii* var. *davyana

This succulent plant produces leaves that are shiny green above with white spots arranged in bands, and green below. Short brown spines are present on the leaf margins. It flowers in mid-winter from June to July. It is found in rocky areas in open or slightly shady areas throughout the COH.

NANA-BERRY

Rhus dentata

These trees grow from 1–5 m in height. The leaves vary in size, and are usually hairy with toothed margins. The young leaves are coppery, and the flowers are small and yellow. They bloom from August to November. They are found in forest margins, rocky outcrops and scrub in the COH.

SILVER VERNONIA

Vernonia natalensis

This is a perennial forb growing to a height of approx-

Silver vernonia

River bushwillow

imately 1 metre. The plant is characteristically covered in silvery white hairs and leaves are typically lance-shaped. The flowers are purple and it blooms from spring to summer. This plant is used traditionally to treat coughs, malaria, ensure healthy pregnancy and as a charm against lightning.

RIVER BUSHWILLOW
Combretum erythrophyllum
These trees grow between 5 and 12 m in height. The bark is cream to pale greyish brown, mottled and flaking. The thin, veined leaves appear on short side twigs, and the margins are fringed with hairs. There is a flush of white leaves in spring. The flowers are greenish white. The fruit, which is characterized by four wings, is green, turning brown later in the season.

BLADDER-NUT
Diospyros whyteana
This multi-stemmed tree grows 4 to 7 m in height, with almost black bark. The leaves are wavy and fringed with soft hairs. The flowers are creamy yellow and are enclosed in an inflated, papery calyx.

Wild apricot

WILD APRICOT
Dovyalis zeyheri
This tree may have spines up to 30 mm long, or it may be spineless. The leaves are either alternated or clustered, with the young leaves being velvety. The fruit is oval and smooth. It is found in woodlands and rocky areas in the COH.

Red-leaved rock fig

RED-LEAVED ROCK FIG
Ficus ingens
This tree grows 3 to 12 m tall on rock faces, with the main stem usually straggling. It shows a spectacular spring flush of coppery-red leaves. The leaves normally have yellow veins protruding beneath, but are of variable shape. The figs, found in the leaf axils, are 9–12 mm in diameter, and are smooth pinkish red when ripe.

CHEESEWOOD
Pittosporum viridiflorum
These trees grow from 3–15 m in height, with a dark, rough bark that smells and tastes like

Cheesewood

Bladder-nut flowers

liquorice. The leaves are alternated or clustered, and are variable in size and shape. A triangle of three small dots is clearly visible in broken-off leaf stalks. The flowers are scented and in terminal leaf clusters, appearing from September to November. The profuse fruit is brown when ripe, and splits to expose sticky shiny red seeds. They are widespread throughout the COH.

Common sugarbush

COMMON SUGARBUSH

Protea caffra

These grow to 6 m. The stem is gnarled, with thick, black, fissured bark. Young stems are pink. The leaves are narrow, the flowers large, and the bracts are pink, red or green from October to January. Widespread in grasslands in the COH.

COMMON BRIDE'S BUSH

Pavetta gardeniifolia

These grow to about 6 m, with corky bark and flattened twigs. The leaves are smooth and shiny, tapering abruptly to a blunt tip. When held against the light, dark spots (groups of bacteria) can be seen. They are found in woodlands and rocky hillsides in the COH.

Common bride's bush

COMMON WILD PEAR

Dombeya rotundifolia

This tree grows from 3–5 m tall, with rough, fissured bark. The leaves are round, thick and coarse. The flowers are white or

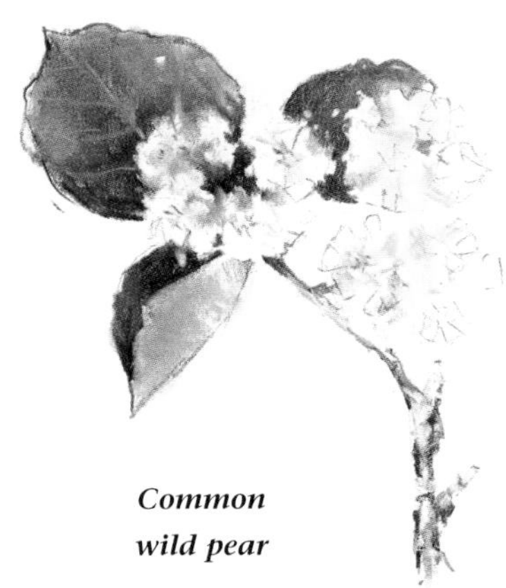

Common wild pear

pink, found in profusion on bare trees from July to September. The fruit is held in a small capsule within old flowers turned brown and papery. Found on open rocky areas.

MOUNTAIN HARD PEAR

Olinia emarginata

This tree grows between 2 and 15 m high, with upward-growing branches. The bark is pale brownish yellow and flaking. Young twigs are square

Mountain hard pear

and the branchlets are a smooth, pale creamy white. The leaf tips are rounded and notched and when crushed have an almond scent. The stalk is pinkish red. The flowers are small and hang in sprays. This tree is found in forest and riverine areas in the COH.

Wild olive

WILD OLIVE

Olea europaea* subsp. *africana

A small- to medium-sized tree growing to about 10 m in height, but sometimes appearing only as a shrub. The grey-green to shiny dark green leaves are narrow and oblong-elliptic in shape and greyish on the undersurface. The small fruit is ovoid and purple-black when ripe. In the COH it is one of the two most common trees found in the mouths of caves or in sinkholes, the other very common tree being *Celtis africana*.

WHITE STINKWOOD

Celtis africana

A beautiful tree often exceeding 30 m in height, it has pale grey to whitish bark and ovate, light to dark green leaves. Often found in the vicinity of caves or actually growing from the mouths of caves and sinkholes, the white stinkwood is a valuable aid to scientists searching for cave sites or underground faults.

White stinkwood

GRASSES AND FERNS

COMMON RUSSET GRASS

Loudetia simplex

This perennial grass grows to about 1,2 m tall. The leaves are flat or rolled, and the nodes ringed with hairs. It flowers from November to January. It is found in open grasslands throughout the COH.

Common russet grass

PELLAEA

Pellaea dolomitica

These medium-sized ferns grow up to about 400 mm in size, with large, tufted fronds. The stalk is dark coloured, and the blades reach about 350 mm in length. The leaflets are more or less triangular, thick, and grey-green. They prefer rocky outcrops, in particular the dolomites of the COH.

Pellaea

CRADLE OF HUMANKIND DIRECTORY

This directory provides information on places of interest and things to do in and around the Cradle of Humankind.

TOURISM INFORMATION

Gauteng Tourism Authority
Tourist information for the province of Gauteng.
Tel: (011) 327 2000
Web: **www.gauteng.net**
E-mail: **tourism@gauteng.net**

Hartbeespoort Dam
A popular destination for weekend getaways and day trips. The web site provides details on places to stay, restaurants and things to do and see.
Web: **www.hartbeespoortdam.com**

Magaliesberg
An online guide to this scenic area that lies within easy reach of Johannesburg and Pretoria.
Web: **www.magaliesberg.co.za**

North West Tourism
Tourist information for North West Province.
Tel: (018) 397 1500
Web: **www.tourismnorthwest.co.za**
E-mail: **tidcpotch@mweb.co.za**

Valley of Ancestors
An online guide to attractions surrounding the Cradle of Humankind.
Web: **www.valleyofancestors.co.za**

PLACES TO STAY

Aloe Ridge Hotel
Luxury accommodation, two restaurants and a cocktail bar. Facilities include an indoor heated pool, an outdoor pool, a floodlit tennis court and an observatory with two telescopes. Trout fishing and game drives can be arranged.
Tel: (011) 957 2070
E-mail: **aloereservations@mweb.co.za**
About 45 minutes outside Johannesburg, off Beyers Naudé Drive.

Amanzingwe Bush Lodge
Specialist wedding venue also catering for corporate and private functions. Sunday buffet lunches. Accommodation consists of 15 freestanding suites, each with its own sundeck. Game drives can be arranged by appointment.
Tel: (012) 205 1108
Web: **www.amanzingwe.co.za**
E-mail: **info@amanzingwe.co.za**
Located in Broederstroom, just south of the Hartbeespoort Dam

Apricot Hill Farm
Self-catering cottages and B&B with spectacular views of Magaliesberg and Swartkop. Sunset barbeques, walks and birdwatching.
Tel: (011) 662 1071 or 082 551 2207
Web: **home.metroweb.co.za/~apricothill**
E-mail: **apricothill@metroweb.co.za**
Situated about 10 km from Sterkfontein caves and 15 km from Krugersdorp centre.

Brookwood Trout Farm
Three trout dams overlooking scenic valley. Day visitors welcome. Wheelchair friendly. Accommodation in self-catering cottages. Camping facilities.
Tel/Fax: (011) 957 0126 or David 082 856 2448 (regarding fishing)
From the M5 take the D374 past Pete-Z-Area and Glenburn Lodge.

Cradle Lodge
Thatched country retreat on 36 ha overlooking the World Heritage Site. Luxury suites with separate lounge and bathroom, mini bar and TV.
Tel: (011) 956 6206 or 082 575 1736 (Brian)
Fax: (011) 956 6207
E-mail: **karkieboss@hotmail.com**
2 km north of Sterkfontein caves

Cradle Nature Reserve, The
A 3 000-hectare private nature reserve, set at the edge of the Magaliesberg in the Cradle of Humankind World Heritage Site. Restaurant Cornuti offers fine dining with spectacular views. Self-catering wood and thatch A-frame chalets are set beside a stream underneath shady trees.
Tel: (011) 659 1622
Fax: (011) 701 3206
Web: **www.thecradle.co.za**
E-mail: **enquiries@thecradle.co.za**
Situated within the Cradle of Humankind.

Croco Lodge and Function Venue
Thatched lodge with 17 luxurious bedroom suites. The Safari Pub and Croco Cellar offer *à la carte* and pub lunches, while the traditional Cape dishes and potjiekos can be had at the Plaaskombuis Restaurant.
Tel: (011) 662 1913
Web: **www.crocolodge.co.za**
E-mail: **croco@worldonline.co.za**
On Featherbrooke Estate off the R28 Pretoria–Krugersdorp highway.

Discover Lodge, The
Conference centre, restaurant and 13 luxury double bedrooms. Game drives, horse trails and an enormous walk-in indigenous Bird Aviary in Africa. Organised 4x4 activities.
Tel: (011) 952 1970/1/2
Fax: (011) 952 1977
Web: **www.discoverlodge.co.za**
E-mail: **info@discoverlodge.co.za**
Situated in Krugersdorp West, bordering Krugersdorp Nature Reserve.

Eagle Guest Lodge
B&B or self-catering cottages, fully equipped and serviced. Abundant bird life, horse riding and swimming on property. Tennis, golf, game drives and trout fishing nearby.
Tel: (011) 659 0004 or 082 472 4614
Situated at the end of Beyers Naudé Drive, about 20 minutes' drive from Sterkfontein caves.

Garden Lodge, The
Cosy hotel rooms set in beautiful gardens. Restaurant offers English pub lunch or *à la carte* for Sunday lunch, depending on number of guests in hotel.
Tel: (011) 745 0400/1/2
Fax: (011) 745 0500
Web: **www.gardenlodge.co.za**
E-mail: **info@gardenlodge.co.za**
Situated off the M5 Beyers Naudé extension.

Glen Afric Country Lodge
A private wildlife sanctuary offering game drives in open Land Rovers. Accommodation includes a luxury lodge, bush and tented camps.
Tel: (012) 205 1412 or 205 1994
Web: **www.glenafric.co.za**
E-mail: **glenafric@icon.co.za**
Off the Pelindaba road, about 5 minutes' drive away from Hartbeespoort Dam.

Glenburn Lodge
Conference rooms, chalets, hotel rooms and luxury suites. Recreational facilities include hot-air ballooning, horse trails, walking trails, adventure golf course, river trout fishing, floodlit tennis.
Tel: (011) 957 2691
Web: **www.glenburn.co.za**
E-mail: **glenburn@glenburn.co.za**
Situated close to Muldersdrift, off Beyers Naudé Drive.

Hakunamatata
A 21-acre estate with modern conference and function facilities, luxurious lodge accommodation and a rejuvenating health spa.
Tel: (011) 794 2588
Fax: (011) 794 2588
Web: **www.hakunamatata.com**
E-mail: **hakunamatata@gem.co.za**
Off Beyers Naudé Drive, about 10 km before Krugersdorp.

Heia Safari Ranch
The 3-star hotel offers 45 bungalows. Every Sunday a barbeque lunch is followed by the Mzumba Tribal Dancers. Authentic Zulu village with traditional Zulu dance/meal. Conferences/functions for up to 100 delegates.
Tel: (011) 659 0605/6/7/8
Fax: (011) 650 0709
Web: **www.heia-safari.co.za**
E-mail: **heia@netactive.co.za**
From Johannesburg, left off the Beyers Naudé extension road 5 km after crossing the R28 highway.

Hippo Guest Lodge
Fully equipped and furnished self-catering chalets set in secure and spacious wooded surrounds. Pool and tennis court on the property; horse riding, game drives, trout fishing and country restaurant close by.
Tel: (011) 659 0770 or 082 928 3159
E-mail: **geofmaud@global.co.za**
10 Pine Valley Road, Lammermoor.

La Chaumiere Guest House
Accommodation in luxurious family home set in lush, park-like gardens. Picnic baskets or light lunches can be arranged.
Tel: (012) 205 1007 or 083 624 9642
Web: **www.lachaumiere.co.za**
E-mail:
LaChaumiere@freemail.absa.co.za

Leopard Lodge
A private game farm nestled in the Magaliesberg. Double rooms, chalets, a self-contained thatched house and conference rooms are available.
Tel: (012) 207 1130 or 083 267 6406
Web: **www.leopardlodge.co.za**
E-mail: **info@leopardlodge.co.za**

Little Foot Manor
Superior self-catering accommodation (from single rondavels to three-bedroom/two-bathroom units).
Tel: (011) 956 6452 or 083 670 1777
E-mail: **kinglouis@icon.co.za**
Situated 8 km from the Sterkfontein caves.

Loosen's Game Lodge
Offers guided game drives, self-catering cottages, and hikes, an exquisite venue for small weddings, day conferences, workshops, team building and functions. Stunning views of wooded valleys, the Schurweberg range and the Magaliesberg.
Tel: (011) 701 3587 or 082 570 5413 or 082 823 1187
Web: **www.loosen-lodge.com**
E-mail:
loosensgamelodge@worldonline.co.za

Makalani Resort
Self-catering chalets, B&B units and camping sites. Swimming pools, trampolines, restaurant, bird park and conference facilities.
Tel/Fax: (012) 253 0436 or 082 765 0413
Web: **www.hartbeespoortdam.com/makalani**

Mount Grace Hotel
Eighty double bedrooms and two restaurants. Tennis, hiking, swimming, mountain biking, trout fishing, and birdwatching on the premises.
Tel: (014) 577 1350
Fax: (014) 577 1202
Web: **www.grace.co.za**
Outside Magaliesberg on the old Rustenburg road.

Ngonyama Lion Lodge
Private game reserve with lion, rhino, cheetah, buffalo, hippo, giraffe and more than 28 other species. Facilities include: self-catering and B&B accommodation, with bar, restaurant, swimming pool, day visitors' picnic area and caravan park.
Tel: (011) 950 9900
Fax (011) 665 1735
Web: **www.afribush.co.za**
E-mail:
info@afribush.co.za
Off the R24, outside Krugersdorp.

Oberon Holiday Resort
Waterside log chalets, fully equipped self-catering accommodation, tented safari camp, caravan park and pool, fishing, boating (launch slipways), braai areas, game and bird watching, serviced ablution and laundry facilities. Day visitors welcome.
Tel: (012) 244 1353 or 082 785 3471
Web:
www.hartbeespoortdam.com/oberon
E-mail:
oberon@hartbeespoortdam.com
Situated on the banks of the Hartbeespoort Dam.

Ou Pastorie Guest House & Restaurant
Historic 121-year-old homestead offers four garden suites. Breakfast and lunch served. During the week, dinner by reservation only.
Tel: (012) 207 1027 or 207 1091
Web: **www.dieoupastorie.com**
E-mail: **oupastorie@mweb.co.za**
R560 route, Skeerpoort.

Rhino & Lion Nature Reserve
Private game reserve with lion, rhino, cheetah, hippo, wild dogs and more than 20 other species. Facilities include picnic area, restaurant, pub, kiosk, animal crèche, reptile and education centre, swimming pool, self-catering accommodation in fully equipped chalets and upmarket safari camp. Every weekend live snake displays and lion, cheetah and wild dog feeding (enquire for times). Game drives and horse trails.
Tel: (011) 957 0109 or 957 0106
Web: **www.rhinolion.co.za**
E-mail: **hippo@global.co.za**
Situated off the Kromdraai road.

Ring Oxwagon Inn, The
Accommodation offered in beautifully restored oxwagons and backpackers' inn. Includes a venue for Christian camps, conference facilities, and a rock pool and hiking trail.
Tel: (012) 259 1506 or 259 0200 or 082 634 4982

Segwati Ranch
Fully equipped self-catering accommodation. Activities include bird watching, walking, swimming, picnicking, hiking and mountain-biking, game drives and team-building facilities.
Tel: (012) 207 1058 or 082 557 3242
Fax: (011) 708 1711
Web: **www.segwatiranch.co.za**
E-mail: **info@segwatiranch.co.za**
About 10 minutes' drive away from Hartbeespoort Dam.

Shumba Valley Lodge
Country lodge with 60 thatched ethnic-decor suites and rooms and five conference rooms. Pub and *à la carte* restaurant.
Tel: (011) 790 8000
Fax: (011) 659 0590
Web: **www.shumbavalley.co.za**
E-mail: **shumbavalley@mweb.co.za**
Situated on the extension of Hans Strydom Avenue (Pelindaba road), just before Lanseria Airport.

Sterkfontein Heritage Lodge
Overlooking the Sterkfontein Valley, this rustic farm homestead offers ten double rooms and two conference rooms. Cocktail lounge and restaurant.
Tel: (011) 956 6307
Web: **www.sterkfonteinlodge.com**
E-mail: **lodge@sterkfontein1.com**

Subroview Country House and Peter's Bistro
Beautiful cottages overlooking the Magaliesberg. Breakfast, light lunches and *à la carte* restaurant. Booking essential.
Tel: (011) 952 2977 or 952 2769 or 082 828 1344 (Peter)
Web: **www.subroview.co.za**
E-mail: **surber@netactive.co.za**
On the N14 between Oaktree and Tarlton, near the Krugersdorp Game Reserve, 62 Pieterstraat, Beckedan.

Tandile
Quaint thatched self-catering cottage set in 20 hectares of bushland.
Tel: 082 537 5658
E-mail: **jennyjen@netactive.co.za**
In Broederstroom, off the Pelindaba road, about 5 minutes' drive away from Hartbeespoort Dam.

Toadbury Hall
Country hotel and restaurant set in lush English gardens. A function hall for corporate and private parties is offered as well as conference facilities. Picnic baskets made to order can be enjoyed on the banks of the Crocodile River.
Tel: (011) 659 0335
Web: **www.toadburyhall.co.za**
E-mail: **enquiries@toadbury.co.za**
Situated about 11 km off the R28 towards Lindley.

Tunstall Farm Guest House
Luxury B&B accommodation, and self-catering cottage, set in 100 acres of bushveld with fantastic views, and great walks. Meals on terrace at the pool, in Cradle of Humankind/Rhenosterspruit Nature Reserve.
Tel: (011) 659 1212
Web: **www.travel.to/tunstall.co.za**
E-mail: **tunstall.guesthouse@freemail.absa.co.za**

Waaigras Cottage
Self-catering accommodation overlooking Rhenosterspruit Nature Reserve. Hikes and horse rides (by arrangement), bird watching (298 species).
Tel: (011) 701 3176
Web: **home.global.co.za/~jhorn/waaigras**
E-mail: **duigan@global.co.za**

RESTAURANTS

Goblin's Cove
A three-storey thatch building covered with beautiful life-size murals, and sculptures of a fairy/goblin world set within a small forest and alongside a small man-made lake. Country cuisine.
Tel: (014) 576 2143
Web: **www.goblins.co.za**
E-mail: **www.goblins@worldonline.co.za**
Take the R563 19 km past Sterkfontein caves, turn left into Bekkerschools Road.

Legends
Light lunches, prepared picnics and braai packs in shady gardens on the banks of the Magalies River.
Tel: (014) 577 1223
Fax: (014) 577 2173
Web: **www.hornbill.co.za**
On the R563 at the junction with Bekkerschools Road.

Squires on the Dam
Overlooking Hartbeespoort Dam, with an extensive *à la carte* menu for lunch and supper. Eight double rooms also available.
Tel: (012) 253 1001
Web: **www.hartbeespoortdam.com/squires**
E-mail: **upcc@global.co.za**
Just outside Hartbeestpoort.

Teaspoon & Tankard
A traditional English country restaurant, with an *à la carte* menu

and good selection of draught beers. *En suite* bedrooms available for B&B guests.
Tel: (011) 957 2912
E-mail: **boros@mweb.co.za**
Off Beyers Naudé Drive, 8 km outside Honeydew.

THINGS TO DO

Bill Harrop's Original Balloon Safaris
Hot-air balloon flights over the scenic Magalies River Valley near Hartbeespoort Dam.
Tel: (011) 705 3201 or 082 379 5296
Fax: (011) 705 3202
Web: **www.balloon.co.za**
E-mail: **info@balloon.co.za**

Brookwood Trout Farm
Three trout dams overlooking scenic valley. Day visitors welcome. Wheelchair friendly. Accommodation in self-catering cottages.
Tel: (011) 957 0126 or 082 856 2448
From the M5 take the D374 past Pete-Z-Area and Glenburn Lodge.

Country Horse Trails
Scenic routes with gentle-natured horses. Experience swimming on horseback in a nearby game park or a moonlight ride.
Tel: (012) 244 1003 or 082 437 8087
Situated south of Hartbeespoort Dam.

Crocodile Ramble
A guide to restaurants, places to stay, art and craft venues, and other activities based in the Cradle of Humankind.
Tel: (011) 957 3742
Web: **www.crocodileramble.co.za**
E-mail: **info@crocodileramble.co.za**

Danielsrust Horse Trails
Guided out-ride options on one of the last remaining big game farms in Gauteng, or horseback safaris viewing rhino, buffalo and more than 20 other game species on trained, groomed horses. No experience necessary.
Booking essential.
Tel: (011) 957 0034
Within 5 km of Sterkfontein caves.

De Wildt Cheetah Centre
Breeding centre for cheetah and wild dog. Guided tours in open/shaded vehicle available. Public tours are about three hours long. We also offer school tours and family walking tours (1,5 hours), as well as the 'Reach for the Wild' sensory trail for disabled people. Advance booking essential (no casual visitors or children under six). Cheetah Lodge located nearby provides lunch by prior booking only and offers a DB&B package.
Tel: (012) 504 1921
Web: **www.dewildt.org.za**
E-mail: **cheetah@dewildt.org.za**
Close to Hartbeespoort Dam, off the R513.

Elephant Sanctuary, The
Home to six African elephants. Day programmes allow you to walk with, touch and feed the elephants. Accommodation available in a 10-bed Indo-African lodge.
Tel: (012) 258 0423
Web: **www.elephantsanctuary.co.za**
E-mail: **elephantsanctuary@mweb.co.za**

Featherheads Creek Paintball Range
A paintball range catering for over 20 people per game. Latest equipment supplied.
Tel: (011) 763 3186 or 082 895 5938
E-mail: **mike@wargames.co.za**
In Muldersdrift, off Hendrik Potgieter Road.

Flying Pictures Pty Ltd
Hot-air balloon flights daily over the Cradle of Humankind.
Tel: (011) 957 2322/3 or 082 325 4796
Fax: (011) 957 2464
Web: **www.hotairballoons.co.za**
E-mail: **flypixsa@iafrica.com**

Garden World
The lush grounds of Garden World surround an extensive garden centre, rustic tea garden, a stunningly different wedding venue, and a children's animal farm. A Sunday craft market incorporates country furniture.
Tel: (011) 957 2046/7/8
Fax: (011) 957 3214
Banqueting fax: (011) 957 2545
Web: **www.gardenworld.co.za**
E-mail: **nursery@gardenworld.co.za**
Beyers Naudé (DF Malan) Drive ext, Muldersdrift.

Hartbeespoort Aquarium
Home to a variety of freshwater fish, birds and animals. Open daily 8:30 am to 5 pm.
Tel: (012) 259 0080 or 082 469 2979
Web: **www.hartbeespoort.com**
Situated in Hartbeespoort.

Hennops Off-Road Trail
A 4x4 trail for both novice and experienced drivers. Herds of zebra, blue wildebeest and blesbok as well as a wide variety of bird life and smaller animals can be viewed along the way. Open weekends and public holidays.
Tel: (012) 371 9360 or Werner 082 825 9205
Web: **www.hennops.co.za**
E-mail: **info@hennops.co.za**
Off the R511 to Brits.

Hennops Picnic Spot & Hiking Trail
Picnic spots, braai areas and swimming pools located on the river banks. Two-day hiking trail sets off from two bush camps. Trails meander alongside the river before they veer away into the surrounding mountains. Day hikers are welcome.
Tel: (012) 371 9360 or 082 566 5037
E-mail: **info@hennops.co.za**
Off the R511 to Brits.

James Kitching Gallery
The Bernard Price Institute maintains this small but stellar museum of palaeontology, featuring fossils of the earliest dinosaurs and mammals, as well as ancient tortoises. Open Monday to Friday from 8:30 am to 4:30 pm.
Tel: 011 717 6682
E-mail: **bpipal@geosciences.wits.ac.za**
In the Van Riet Lowe Building on the East Campus of the University of the Witwatersrand in Braamfontein.

Lion Park
More than 50 lions, including a rare white lion, can be viewed from vehicles in four camps. Other large carnivores include cheetah, leopard and wild dog. Facilities include picnic sites, camping tents, a restaurant and curio shop.
Tel: (011) 460 1814
Fax: (011) 460 1061 or 460 1631
Web: **www.lion-park.com**
E-mail: **lionpark@cknet.co.za**
Corner Hans Strijdom and R55.

Old Kromdraai Gold Mine
One of the first gold mines on the Witwatersrand, dating back to 1881. Guided tours on the hour. Tuesday to Friday by appointment only.
Tel: (011) 957 0211
Fax: (011) 957 0205

Paddle Power Adventures
Grade 1, 2 and 3 rapids suitable for both novice and experienced canoeists. A day trip covers roughly 15 km with no less than 16 rapids, and a picnic lunch is served alongside the river. Mountain bike, horse and hiking trails also available.
Tel: (011) 794 3098 or
082 742 1922/082 956 3597
Web: **www.easyinfo.co.za**
E-mail: **padpower@lantic.net**

SA National Bird of Prey Centre
This centre is situated within the Rhino & Lion Nature Reserve in the Cradle of Humankind. Flying demonstration with owls, eagles, falcons and hawks lasts 45 minutes. Open daily except Mondays.
Tel: 083 585 9540
Web: **www.birdofprey.org.za**
E-mail: **raptor@icon.co.za**

Walter Sisulu National Botanical Garden
Covering almost 300 hectares, the Garden consists of both landscaped and natural veld areas. Eagle's Fare restaurant, situated in the heart of the Garden in the shade of two magnificent white stinkwood trees, serves breakfasts, teas and lunches.
Tel: (011) 958 1750
Web: **www.nbi.ac.za/frames/wits fram.htm**
E-mail: **info@sisulugarden.co.za**
Malcolm Road, Poortview, Roodepoort.

Wild Cave Adventures
Adventure caving expeditions, including abseiling into caves and tailor-made tours.
Tel: (011) 956 6197 or
082 632 1718/082 486 2464
Web: **www.wildcaves.co.za**
E-mail: **info@wildcaves.co.za**

Wonder Cave Show Cave
A natural wonder 2 200 million years old with formations 15 m high, cave pearls, rimstone pools and stalactites. Tours run daily every hour on the hour by experienced guides. Kiosk/curio shop. Enter by lift, no crawling necessary. Abseiling also available by booking.
Tel: (011) 957 0034
Web: **www.conservtours.com**
E-mail: **info@conservtours.com**
About 2,5 km from the Kromdraai–Broederstroom Road.

ARTS AND CULTURE

Baldwin's Art Jewellery Gallery
Handcrafted art jewellery, miniature furniture, paintings and other handmade arts and crafts.
Tel: (012) 253 1854
E-mail: **linki@artjewellery.com**
Situated in Hartbeespoort.

Dietmar Wiening Art Gallery
Dietmar is South Africa's leading bronze sculptor of marine life and birds. Visit this spectacular gallery perched over the Crocodile River, only 40 minutes from Sandton or Pretoria. Worldwide shipping service available. Open every weekend or public holiday 9am–5pm or by appointment.
Tel: (012) 205 1193 or
082 891 9987
Web: **www.dietmarwiening.com**
E-mail:
info@dietmarwiening.co.za
R512/Lanseria road, Broederstroom.

Hartbeespoort Art Gallery
Exhibits work by South African and international artists.
Tel: (012) 253 2915
Web: **www.wildlifegallery.co.za**
Situated in Hartbeespoort.

Lesedi Cultural Village
A cultural village, craft market, restaurant, function venue, conference centre and accommodation in traditional tribal huts. Open daily.
Tel: (012) 205 1394
Fax: (012) 205 1433
Web: **www.lesedi.com**
E-mail: **marketing@lesedi.com**
Situated in Broederstroom, just off the R512.

Mukondeni African Art Gallery
Exclusively South African art gallery set in landscaped gardens. The gallery also commissions artists to create unique items.
Tel: (011) 708 2116
Fax: (011) 708 0194
Web: **www.mukondeni.com**
E-mail: **info@mukondeni.com**
36 Orleans Rd, Kya Sands, Randburg.

Shed Gift and Craft Shop, The
Gifts for both local and international tourists, and to suit all budgets.
Open seven days a week.
Tel: (011) 957 0034
On the premises of the Kromdraai Conservancy Booking Office, on the Sterkfontein caves road.

TOURS

Conserv Tours
Specialists in the Cradle of Humankind and surrounding areas. Tours include a variety of attractions, visits to fossil sites and personalized tours on request. Shuttles from nearby hotels and further afield. Always in the presence of an experienced Deat guide while on tour. Adventure activities include abseiling, game drives, moutain biking, horse trails.
Tel: (011) 957 0034
Web: **www.conservtours.co.za**
E-mail: **info@conservtours.com**
On the Sterkfontein caves road.

Geological Heritage Tours
Flexible, geologically oriented day tours to the Cradle of Humankind, and other sites of interest in the vicinity of the World Heritage Site. Emphasis is on seeing palaeontological, geological and historical gold mining sites, but tours include places of cultural and historical interest, and wildlife attractions. Personalised tours available.

Telefax: (011) 886 8722 or 083 289 4039
Web: **www.geosites.co.za**
E-mail: **geologysites@mweb.co.za**
PO Box 943, Pinegowrie, 2123, South Africa.

Hayward's Luxury Safari Events & Expeditions
Set on 30 000 acres of private wilderness, Hayward's camp hosts executive corporate events, teambuilding and adventurous big-group excursions. A safari offers game viewing on horseback, abseiling, flyfishing, archery, caving, biking, 4x4ing, ballooning and enthralling palaeontology/archaeology lectures for groups of 24–120 delegates.
Tel: (011) 442 5640
Web: **www.safaridoctor.co.za**
E-mail: **secluded@iafrica.com**

Honeysuckle Holidays
Offers tours to the Sterkfontein Heritage Site, Lesedi, Elephant Sanctuary, Pretoria, Soweto and Gold Reef City.
Tel: (011) 662 1492 or 083 621 5769
Web: **www.honeysuckle.co.za**
E-mail: **info@honeysuckle.co.za**

Kromdraai Special Interest Hiking Trails
Guided one- or two-day trails in the Kromdraai Conservancy, in the presence of an experienced Satour-registered field guide. Accommodation in rustic hiker's huts or tented camp. Special school tours and fossil talks available. Good bird-watching opportunities.
Tel: 011 957 0241
Web: **www.conservetours.com**
E-mail: **info@conservetours.com**
On the Sterkfontein caves road.

Mogale's Gate
Environmental Education Centre and Bush School. Offers a variety of hands-on educational syllabus-based excursions for school groups, especially for grades four to seven, in the veld.
Tel/Fax: (014) 576 2091 or (014) 576 2375
E-mail: **Willem.Prinsloo@standardbank.co.za**

Palaeo-Tours
Tailor-made tours to the internationally famous fossil sites of Sterkfontein, Swartkrans and Drimolen in the Cradle of Humankind World Heritage Site. All tours are by arrangement only, are conducted by scientists and take into account the interest level and time schedule of the group.
Tel/Fax: (011) 726 8788 or 082 804 2899
Web: **www.palaeotours.com**
E-mail: **palaeotours@mweb.co.za**

Passage to Africa
Ground and aerial tours for the World Heritage Site conducted by palaeontology graduates from Wits University.
Tel: 011 478 2966
E-mail: **africaml@iafrica.com**

PAST (Palaeo-Anthropology Scientific Trust)
Guided field trips for all ages to active fossil excavation sites that combine cave exploration, interactive debates and discussions on site, and a close look at fossils *in situ*, stone artefacts and hominid fossil casts. In addition PAST also offers educational outings to the fossil sites for school and student groups, which can include the unique Walking Tall 'palaeo-theatre' production and hands-on lectures. Tailored for all levels, from primary through to tertiary level.
Tel: (011) 486 3083
Fax: (011) 486 3084
E-mail: **pastscience@iafrica.com**

Westour
West Rand District Municipality Centre supplies information on the marketing and development in the Cradle of Humankind and West Rand.
Tel: (011) 692 2128
Web: **www.wrdm.gov.za**
E-mail: **tourism@wrdm.gov.za**
West Rand District Municipality Centre, Cnr 6th and Park streets, Randfontein.

If you would like your details included in future editions of the Cradle of Humankind field guide, please e-mail cradle@struik.co.za

For more information on Sterkfontein and archaeotourism in the rest of South Africa, contact the following:

Cradle of Humankind Programme
The Department of Agriculture, Conservation, Environment and Land Affairs is presently designated the management authority for the Cradle of Humankind World Heritage Site.
Tel: (011) 355 1400
Web: **www.cradleofhumankind.co.za**
E-mail: **cradleofhumankind@gpg.gov.za**
PO Box 8769, Johannesburg 2000, Gauteng, South Africa

Palaeoanthropology Unit for Research and Exploration (PURE)
The University of the Witwatersrand
Tel: (011) 339 7202
The following sites are open to the public:
Sterkfontein caves: (011) 956 6342
Wonder Cave: (011) 957 0106
Sterkfontein Cave: 9am–4:30pm
Tours leave every half hour, last one at 4:30pm.
Open every day of the year except Christmas Day.

Prime Origins Project
Prime Origins is a media company specializing in South Africa's human and natural heritage. It produces books, booklets and maps for the Cradle of Humankind World Heritage Site, the Kruger National Park and other important tourist attractions.
Web: **www.primeorigins.com**
E-mail: **berger@icon.co.za**

Sterkfontein Research Unit
Based at the University of the Witwatersrand
Tel: (011) 717 2516

BIBLIOGRAPHY

Acocks, JPH. 1988. *Veld Types of South Africa.* Memoirs of the Botanical Survey of South Africa. National Botanical Institute of SA.

Berger, LR & Hilton-Barber, B. 2000. *In the Footsteps of Eve.* Washington DC: National Geographic Adventure Press.

Brain, CK. (i) 1981. *The Hunters or the Hunted?* Chigaco: University of Chicago Press.

Brain, CK. (ii) 1998. 'The Swartkrans Cave Site'. In *Dual Congress Guide Book.*

Bredenkamp, G & Van Rooyen, N. 1996. 'Rocky Highveld Grassland'. Chapter in *Vegetation of South Africa, Lesotho and Swaziland.* Department of Environmental Affairs and Tourism.

Broom, R & Schepers, GWH. 1946. *The South African Fossil Ape-Men, the Australopithicinae.* Pretoria: Transvaal Museum.

Carruthers, VC. 2000. *The Magaliesberg.* Pretoria: Protea Book House.

Carruthers, VC. 2000. *The Wildlife of Southern Africa.* Cape Town: Struik.

Clarke, R. 1998. First Ever Discovery of a Well-Preserved Skull and Associated Skeleton of *Australopithecus.* In *SA Journal of Science,* vol. 94 (October).

Dippenaar-Schoeman, AS & Jocque, R. 1997. *African Spiders: an identification manual.* Pretoria: Plant Protection Unit.

Gregory, WK. 1939. 'The South African fossil man-apes and the origin of the human dentition'. In *Journal of the American Dental Association,* vol. 26.

Hall, M. 1987. *The Changing Past: Farmers, Kings and Traders in Southern Africa, 200–1860.* Cape Town: David Philip.

Haltenorth, T & Diller, H. 1986. *A field guide to the mammals of Africa, including Madagascar.* London: Collins.

Hamilton, C. ed. 1995. *The Mefecane Aftermath (Reconstruction Debates in Southern African History).* Wits University Press and University of Natal Press.

Hammond-Tooke, D. 1993. *The Roots of Black South Africa.* Johannesburg: Jonathan Ball Publishers.

Huffman, T. 1989. *Iron Age Migrations.* Johannesburg: Wits University Press.

Maclean, GL. 1993. *Roberts' Birds of Southern Africa.* Cape Town: John Voelker Bird Book Fund.

Mason, R. 1962. *Prehistory of the Transvaal.* Johannesburg: Witwatersrand University Press.

A mandible of Paranthropus robustus *from Drimolen.* (GG)

Palgrave, KC. 1988. *Trees of Southern Africa.* Cape Town: Struik.

Passmore, NI & Carruthers, VC. 1995. *South African Frogs.* Johannesburg: Witwatersrand University Press.

Perry, W. (Spring 1999). *An* 'Archaeological Text of the Settler Model Account of the Mfeqane/Difaqane'. In *Africa Update,* vol. VI, issue 2.

SABC (South African Broadcasting Corporation). No date given. Beyond Antiquity. A series of radio lectures on the origin of man, arranged by Raymond Dart.

Sinclair, I. 1987. *Field Guide to the Birds of Southern Africa.* Cape Town: Struik.

Skinner, JD & Smithers, RHN. 1990. *The Mammals of the Southern African Subregion.* Pretoria: University of Pretoria.

Terry, R. 1974. *Taung Anniversary Booklet.* Johannesburg: Witwatersrand University Press.

Tobias, P. 1994. 'Ad Hominidae: The Future of South Africa's Ancient Past'. In *Optima,* vol. 40, no. 1 (April).

Van Wyk, B & Malan, S. 1988. *Field Guide to the Wild Flowers of the Highveld.* Cape Town: Struik.

Van Wyk, E & Van Oudtshoorn, F. 1999. *Guide to the Grasses of South Africa.* Pretoria: Briza.

Walton, J. 1956. *An African Village.* Pretoria: JL van Schaik Ltd.

Wilson, M. 1969. *The Thousand Years before Van Riebeeck (Raymond Dart Lecture Series).* Johannesburg: Witwatersrand University Press.

GLOSSARY

Acheulean a stone tool industry found at Swartkrans in the Cradle of Humankind, dating from about 1,7 mya to approximately 250 000 years ago. It is often characterized by teardrop-shaped handaxes.

apartheid the policy of racial segregation practised by the former white minority government of South Africa.

ape-man a general term used to refer to the australopithecines. A hominin that is more 'ape' than 'human'. The term 'man-ape' is sometimes used to describe the ape-men who were beginning to display more advanced features associated with our genus, *Homo*.

arboreal adapted to living in trees.

Archaen rocks formed in the Precambrian era.

archaeology the study of the past by scientific analysis of the material remains of human culture.

archaic something ancient, belonging to a much earlier era. Frequently used in association with more primitive forms of our own species, *Homo sapiens*.

aridification the process of becoming drier. Generally refers to climatic periods during which the environment became drier.

artefact something made by humans. Both a stone tool and a painting are artefacts.

assemblages a number of material remains gathered together. In archaeology an assemblage usually refers to a grouping of tools or fossils.

Australopithecus a genus of hominin that first appeared about 4 mya and went extinct about 1 mya. Often split into two forms: robust and gracile. The gracile form was characterized by finer facial features, while the robust form can be recognized by its enormous jaws and teeth.

Bantu a term now used to describe people whose linguistic rootstock evolved from central Africa several thousand years ago; historically it has negative connotations because the former South African government labelled all black people as Bantus.

bipedalism the ability to walk on two legs. All hominins are bipedal.

bovid a member of the family Bovidae. Ruminants such as antelope are bovids.

breccia the consolidated matrix that fills a cave. It consists of sediments, rock fragments, and often bone, which are cemented together with lime to form a concrete-like rock.

calcium carbonate (CaCo3) a general term for lime. Lime precipitates from dolomite.

cranial capacity the volume of the brain cavity.

Difaqane A period of social turbulence and volatility that created upheaval for the Sotho-Tswana-speaking communities of the southern African highveld during the early 19th century. Whether or not the Difaqane was a direct consequence of the Mfeqane is a subject of debate among historians.

DNA deoxyribonucleic acid, the main constituent of a chromosome. DNA is responsible for the transmission of hereditary characteristics. Mitochondrial DNA is passed through the female line only and is the most common form of DNA used to calculate the date of origin of modern humans.

dolomite an ancient rock that formed in shallow seas, consisting of lime, magnesium, and other trace minerals. Common in the Cradle of Humankind and the bedrock in which caves form.

ESR (Electronic Spin Resonance) a dating method based on the fact that tooth enamel is subjected to environmental radiation, which causes electrons to be displaced and become trapped in defect sites. An ESR spectrometer detects the position of these electrons, and the type of signal indicates the dose of radiation received by the buried tooth, from which the presumed age of the fossil can be deduced.

evolution the gradual process of biological change in nature.

fossil a representation of a plant or animal that existed in the past. In order for an organism to become a fossil, scientists generally agree that the process of mineralization must have occurred.

genus a taxonomic group that divides a family and contains one or more species.

Gondwana one of the two ancient supercontinents produced by the split of Pangea, comprising what are now Africa, South America, Australia, Antarctica and the Indian subcontinent.

habilines a collective term used to describe members of the species *Homo habilis*.

Holocene a time period dating from around 10 000 years ago to the present.

hominids bipedal apes that are found in the family tree of humankind. Scientists today generally refer to the hominids as 'hominins'.

hominins *see* 'hominids'.

hominoids a taxonomic group encompassing African apes and humans.

hunter-gatherers people whose lifestyle and subsistence practices are dominated by hunting and gathering from the land, as opposed to pastoralists or agriculturalists.

in situ in place.

Iron Age In Africa, the Iron Age dates from about 2 000 years ago to the late 18th century. It was an era characterized by the use of metals for weapons and tools, and in southern Africa it is associated with the arrival of migrant pastoralists from central Africa.

kiln a large oven designed to fire pottery.

Laurasia one of the two ancient supercontinents produced by the split of Pangea, comprising what are now North America, Greenland, Europe and Asia.

Magaliesberg the range of mountains to the north and northwest of the Cradle of Humankind, named after the Po chief Mogale.

Member a geological term used to distinguish different levels or strata in cave infills. There are five main Members at Sterkfontein.

Mfeqane a time of intense and bloody social turmoil at the beginning of the 19th century when Zulu expansionism had a knock-on effect on almost all the tribes living in southern Africa.

microlith a small, retouched tool.

Miocene a time period lasting from about 25 mya to about 5 mya.

morphology the form or structure of an organism or its parts.

Oldowan the earliest commonly recognized tool industry, dating from around 2,6 mya to about 1,7 mya.

osteodontokeratic culture the bone (osteo), tooth (donto) and horn (keratic) culture, so designated by Raymond Dart to express what he believed to be the earliest culture adopted by hominins. Later discarded as having no archaeological basis.

palaeoanthropology the study of ancient humans and their culture.

palaeontology the study of ancient life forms.

Pangea the ancient supercontinent comprising all the ancient continents joined together. It split into two smaller supercontinents about 200 mya.

paranthropines a general term referring to all the so-called robust australopithecines that are members of the genus *Paranthropus*.

pastoralists people whose lifestyle is characterized by the herding of animals, usually cattle and/or goats.

Pleistocene a time period dating from around 1,6 mya to about 10 000 years ago.

Pliocene a time period dating from around 5 mya to about 1,6 mya.

Plio-Pleistocene the temporal period from approximately 2,5 to 1 mya. A period of transition between the Pliocene and the Pleistocene.

postcranial the bones or parts of the body from the neck down. Literally 'below the head'.

precipitation the point at which a dissolved substance, for example lime, separates from a solution, for example water.

prognathic to jut out. In hominins, it means that the face juts forward, as in apes.

San a term used to describe the hunter-gatherer communities formerly known as 'Bushmen' who occupied much of the central interior before the arrival of immigrants from elsewhere in the north of Africa and from Europe. Some geneticists believe the San are humanity's last living link with Stone Age populations.

sediments sand or material that has been deposited by slow settling in water.

sexual dimorphism the shape difference between males and females of the same species.

shaman a spiritual leader providing the living link between a community and its ancestors.

speciation the process of changing from one species to another.

species any of the taxonomic grouping into which a genus is divided. Members of a species can only breed with other members of that species.

stromatolite the fossilized remains of an ancient blue-green algae colony. Living colonies still exist in some places today.

taphonomy the study of the grave. It is the science of the reconstruction of the history of fossils and other bones from the time of an organism's death to the time of its discovery.

terrestrial living or moving on the ground.

type site the site where a type specimen was found; generally used to describe a specific culture or style.

First row, left to right: View across John Nash Nature Reserve; the rainbow trout farm; Swartkrans. Second row, left to right: Iron Age enclosure in John Nash Nature Reserve; view of Johannesburg from the COH; Hartbeespoort Dam. Third row, left to right: Giant chert outcrop; game in the Rhino & Lion Nature Reserve; Gladysvale. Last row: Spring eye at the John Nash Nature Reserve (left) and at Plover's Lake (right).

INDEX

Page references in italics indicate illustrations and photographs.